To Chris,
for showing me the other Ways of Being

THE WAY OF DOG

ZANA FRAILLON

Illustrated by
Sean Buckingham

Chicken House

2 Palmer Street, Frome, Somerset BA11 1DS
www.chickenhousebooks.com

First published by University of Queensland Press, PO Box 6042, St Lucia, Queensland 4067 Australia. All rights reserved.

First published in Great Britain in 2023
Chicken House
2 Palmer Street
Frome, Somerset BA11 1DS
United Kingdom
www.chickenhousebooks.com

Chicken House/Scholastic Ireland, 89E Lagan Road, Dublin Industrial Estate, Glasnevin, Dublin D11 HP5F, Republic of Ireland

Cover design by Hannah Janzen and Helen Crawford-White
Cover and interior illustrations by Sean Buckingham
Author photograph by Julian Frallion
Typeset by Post Pre-press Group, Brisbane
Printed and bound in Great Britain by CPI Group (UK) Ltd, Croydon CR0 4YY

FSC
www.fsc.org
MIX
Paper | Supporting
responsible forestry
FSC® C171272

1 3 5 7 9 10 8 6 4 2

British Library Cataloguing in Publication data available.

PB ISBN 978-1-915026-23-1
eISBN 978-1-915026-41-5

The Way of Dog

Dear Shoe-Legs
Are you coming? Are you? Are you?
Then shake wide awake and take my
advice
throw the Burs from your fur and
                              sliiiiiiide on the Ice.
Come flat-foot follow and paw-pad my way
for I have a thing
                  or four
to say about living this life according to
The Way of Dog.

And if you're coming prick your ears
                              pause your paws and
listen sharp
stretch your limbs
swell your lungs with every howl
every scrowl with a full-blown

RRRRRRRROOOOOWWWWWWWLLLLL

for this story is LOUD
it's made to be growled
                  to be bellowed and roared to be
freed from your jaws to
            travel Wind-wide and find those ears and

souls all waiting.

So come scramper
          come trample
come schnuffle about
      come discover this world
from a Dog's point of snout.
Are you coming? Are you? Are you?

THE
BARN

LiFE IS MORE

Be strong. Be fierce. Life is more than a concrete floor.
That is all my mamma yip-yap-yips
that is all she ever says with nubbling nuzzles
                                        lulling licks
with her tail's fwip-fwap-fwip on the thick of
the wire the
            click of her paws the
            whine in her jaws
and the way her heart ROARS
Be strong. Be fierce. Life is more—

            and then we ten pups are rough-grabbed away
to another concrete floor.
Colder
on our little thin-furred bellies
than before.

We wait
            whine and
whimper for our mamma to come
for the warm of her milk the
            silk of her fur on our snouts
but all we get are the shouts
                        from the big GrowlMan to

SHUT IT!
Shoe-legs can be mean.

And in the shadows the Rat kings creep
cutting claws climbing
sharp teeth snipping

> snapping
> grinning at us
> creeping closer to us

and we howl for Mamma

> we waaaooowl-yowl-yip

Are you coming? Are you coming? Are you, Mamma?

> > ***Are***

> > > ***you?***

but she doesn't

> not once

call back.
I guess she's lost her strong
I guess she's lost her fierce
I guess she's learned it's our turn
to be taken. We try not to shake
in the hard empty
cold.

> And those shadows keep creeping closer.

Be strong. Be fierce. Life is more ...
scary without your mamma.

Learnings

In the towers of the cages all around us
is a fear and sad that rages in
                                waves that surround us
and sticks to our fur
like muck.

Where are you, Mamma? Mamma? Mamma?
Where are you? Where are you? Mamma? Mamma?
but no yap
                no grrrrurf
                        no yip
                no awwwouf
                                        no nothing
from our mamma comes back.

Hush the other mammas howl
to all our puppied yearning yowls to
all our calls of confuzzled confusion.
Their conclusions are the same: they are very sure
                                that
Somewhere life is really more
and their knowings down the rows
pass from tongues
                        to ears to
                snouts all sew

The Way of Dog
into our dreamings.

So we ten of us curl and snuggle up tight and
our hearts thumping together
makes us strong
                  makes us fierce
                  makes us

                                        mostly
all right.
Even those Rats aren't so bad after all.
In the light those Rats are
really quite small even though

                                        their teeth
                    are really
                                        quite big
even though there's a fat one that won't stop
his watching.
But we ten pups together are too big for a Rat
no matter how fat
      no matter how sharp his teeth are.

But I guess some of us
just need
more.
I guess some of us
just need
a mamma to squirl in tight close to

and some of us

grow cold

now
some of us

grow hard

now
their beat gone
thrum gone
light in their eyes
breath in their snout

gone.

I guess life isn't *more* for everyone.
That FatRat moves
a little bit closer.

HUNTING HANDS

There were ten of us pups in this cage
to begin with. Now there are eight.
Wait. Seven.
I don't like the way this is going.

The GrowlMan snarls
    angry-fierce eyes gnarled
and we all of us tremble
        shrink-shiver and shake with the
   quake his big
black
    kicking-boots make. That GrowlMan
stomps hard
    fast and
mean.
Waste of money
     he grunts
rough hands hunting the GonePups
snatching the GonePups
       our cage door banging
   clanging
    jamming
slamming

and he hurls those GonePups through the Air

twirls them through the Air

swirls them through the Air

so they land in The Bin. With a

thlunk.

The FatRat grins and
nibbles on the kibble left behind.
Who's next for The Dead-Dog Bin?
he cackles
and we crouch
in the corner of our emptying cage.
I don't like FatRat.
Not one little bit.

CATCHING HAPPINESS

Life is more …

      we yap-yip each other
so we won't lose the wonder
of what is out there

      new there
    through there
        where

          the MammaDogs say
that the Wind whishing by in the big open Sky
    will carry our dreams so high in her wings
that each moment sings only of happy.

    Out there

        where

Trees stretch and
      Clouds loop and SkySingers
          flip-flap-flip-flap-swoop.
We wide-eye their shadows on the walls
    sound-snatch their bwibirling caws and calls
      and we shiver with all that is

          out there.

And there's a peculiar kind of yip
a strange kind of yap
that comes when I trap a shadow for a moment

for a second for
                    a beat
in my paws
                and my jaws open wide in a grrurrrrgle of
happy.
Is this what *The Way of Dog* is?

The other pups try but without a doubt I
am the best pouncer in our cage.

And the shadows on the walls keep
flapping on by and I wonder if
                        out there
        a real SkySinger
is harder to catch than their shadow?

SCRATCHCAT

There is a Cat! A Cat Cat Cat!
A scratchy old Cat that schnuffles of Trees
and of Leaves and of Dirt and of Sunshine.
That Cat licks her paws
                scratches doors with her claws
pads in front of our cages back and
forth back and
forth
her eyes blink long and
         s   l   o   w
her tail flicks to and
fro and there's something in the way she moves
that pokes and stirs that
pushes and whirrs me into a
tangle! And no amount of yip-yap-yipping
of grrrrurfing
                awwwoufing
of pouncing and bouncing of
                clawing and ripping with my
teeth at the wire on my door stops the
tingle in my jaw that comes
                every
                single
                time
that I schnuffle her.
That ScratchCat is all I can think of!

So if I can't chase her then I want to know –
what is the point
of ScratchCat?

CHOOSING FAMILY

FatRat knows a lot about the goings
                              the toings the
    froings of the Barn.
That FatRat's been here foreverer.

He says that the shoe-legs
that visit our cages and *Cooooooooooo*
want us to choose them as
Family.
He tells of the beds where we'd snuggle
and hands that would cuddle and pat us all day.
Every day.
And how we would play and play and play and
That's what Family is, don't you know?

There are 6 of us pups
when the first shoe-legs come.
***Pick me up! I'm your pup! I choose you! Pick me up
pick me up!***

                              Now there are **5** ...

And every day more
shoe-legs come to clutch us away.

Pick me up! I'm your pup! I choose you! Pick me up
pick me up!

4...

Scooped up and cupped up in hands
    held to faces whose traces of living
are so brimming with what

            could *be*

that sometimes the hope of it hurts.
Pick me up! I'm your pup! I choose you! Pick me up
pick me up!

3...

and what is it that I'm doing wrong?

Spin in circles

       FatRat grins.
A good spinner will always bring happiness. That's one
of those MammaDog Ways, don't you know? Trust me,
I'm a Rat.

Huh. I must have missed that.
FatRat takes my food for the tip and
I spin.

2...

I spin for those hands that are just right for me
the schnuffle of my

       soon-to-be Family
    and I think … yes, I'm sure … here they are!
Here they are!

Pick me up! I'm your pup! I choose you! Pick me up
pick me up!
and I'm spinning and twirling their
                    hands on my fur and
          I'm whirling so sure that these are
the hands that will carry me free
                    here they are now
stretching down now
                    reaching round now and—

                    Oh.
                    Never mind. It's
nothing.
Those hands didn't schnuffle right
after all.
I guess.

                                        1.
                                        Just
          1 … just …
                                        me.

SPINNING

I spin while I grow and I spin while I wait alone now on my own now in my cage now. But spinning isn't bringing any happiness at all.

I guess I'm not doing it right.

UNDERSTANDING DOG

Hey there, fella. Are you sick? Why aren't you spinning like usual?

There's a manpup at my cage.
                                He often comes by
always singing while he's sweeping
always laughing while he's cleaning
always sneaking us treats as he changes the pages
on the floors of our cages and he never
bangs or yells at the
whines and whimper-yelps
we all make.
The manpup is not like that GrowlMan at all.

What's the matter, fella? I guess you must be pretty lonely now, huh. Do you wanna come outside for a bit? You're getting too big for that cage.

He opens my door and his
hand on my head is the

                                lick

of my mamma's tongue.

Come on! You know there's a whole big world out there? Life is more than this old cage, you know.

What's that? How can a manpup
made just out of skin
with no paws no

            claws and teeth that can hardly gnaw
with a snout that can't imagine all the schnuffles
in the Breeze

          how can *he* know about
The Way of Dog?
I guess some shoe-legs are just
special like that.

But even though I *want* to go

               I want to *be*

Outside

       my legs are refusing to move.

*Don't be scared. You know me. Did you know I was there
the day you were born? I'm sorry they took your mamma
away like that. They said she was too old for more litters.*

Ohhh. So *that's* what happened to Mamma. Huh.
But where'd she go? Where'd she—

    Listen, kid
          FatRat says from the shadows
    there are some things you just don't want to know …

And the manpup he lifts me
                    right through my cage door and
            my claws dig the floor
and I whimper and whine
and all kinds of feelings are buzzing my mind
because everything is just *so* much more
                            it's all just a little bit
                                        too much
                            too
                frightening.

But then that manpup
he snuggles me tight and he
nuzzles me close his

                snout in my fur and he
        schnuffles me deep
            inside of him. And I
            still. And I quiet.

I know you miss your mamma.
I miss my mamma too. I know
what it's like to be lonely.
You do?
And hey, did I say? I
really love your spinning.
Did you hear that,
FatRat? He says he
loves my spinning!

Manpup gentlies me onto the ground and
I scramper and spin.

       Told you so, kid
                FatRat grins
and I skid
       and I sliiiiiiiiiiide
on that slippery floor
and I follow that manpup
             right up to the door
      and all the way through
to Outside.

THE WAY OF DOG —
MOST MAGNIFICENT

I don't even whine with the sting of the
shine in my eyes
or the burn of the Wind on my skin
and my snout is quivering
                  twitching and
                         all over itching in
             wonder.
In this Outside-of-Barn place
each schnuffle is a whole world of story.

And we play and play and play
                and I show him how I pounce
and he bounces me a ball
that rolls so fast on that Grass —
                 and that Grass is so full
of so many traces
     — and the bouncing ball flies
            so high in the Skies

and I leap up and snap

and I can leap! I can leap!

higher and higher

and I leap so high

I am in the Sky myself!

And my teeth are so strong and
my paws are so tough
that his sock in my jaws will never
be tugged free
from me!
I win every time! This sock is mine!
And I scramper up and down
                              up and down and
           up and down and
                    I could keep running foreverer.

Manpup cuddles and snuggles me tight
with eyes that
                    whisper a million dreams and
skin that schnuffles whole worlds into being and
a face that tastes of the traces of
a million gazillion katrillion
and three places.

And he coos he woos me with treats with meats and
my tongue has never ever everer
                                sung like this before.

                    I suddenly see
what those MammaDogs were on about. Life
really *is* more.
I'm sure I've discovered another *Way of Dog* …
*The Way of Dog – Most Magnificent: The thing that
completes us that beats in our hearts*
                    in our heads

                            in our blood
                            in our bones is …

                                        MEAT.
Meat is A Very Magnificent Thing.
                    The Way of Dog is Meat.

HEAVINESS

It's hard to stay in a cage now I know
what Outside is.
I think that's why my head
                    my heart my
legs all feel so very very heavy every time
Manpup says goodbye.
Don't go! Don't go! Pick me up! I'm your pup!

*Shhhh! My stepdad, Jim, will hear. He can't find out
we play. You know what he's like. Shhhh now. I'll see
you tomorrow.*

I didn't know tomorrows took so long

to arrive.

TRAINING

It's hard to train a manpup whose brain isn't
wired like ours. Sometimes he just doesn't listen.
But I am an excellent teacher and so
that Manpup is slowly learning to know
what I mean when I show him
just what I am wanting.
It has only taken
a few days of training.

Meat! I say and sit and don't move
so he knows I'm A Dog Being Serious.
Manpup laughs and claps his hands
and he scruffles my fur.
Sit! Good boy! Here's a treat! and he gives me meat!

And he knows it is a sign
to say ***That meat is mine***
when I *Sit!* and *Come!* and *Lie!*
and it works every time.
I think I chose him wisely.

I train him to
pat me and hold me and fold me in his body
                    so we can just be
                                    us three
        Meat and Manpup and Me.

THE WAY OF DOG –
TO BE NAMED IS TO BELONG

My stepdad says we don't name the mutts, but what does
he know? I've got the perfect name for you. Scruffity.
What do you think? You're such a ball of fuzz
                    and he scruffles my fur with his snout
Do you like it? Scruffy? Scruff? Scruffity?

Scruffity? Scruffity! That's me! That's me!
I spin spin spin
            I twirl and pounce and
  bounce into his arms
            and just like that
MyManpup and me
are now a
We.

RETHINKING THE WAY

I've been thinking as I wait
                for MyManpup to come
for his schnuffle on the Air for
the warm of his voice
             the brush of his skin on my fur
the whirr of my heart
    and the happy that spreads when
he kisses my head
and he holds me close to his chest
              which is the best feeling
         everer –
I've been thinking
         I think I was
wrong
about *The Way of Dog – Most Magnificent.*

I don't think it *is* meat
that is my treat beyond all others.
I don't think meat is the
dream of Dogs' beings after all.
And I don't know how this can be
but the more I think and think and think the
more I see that
The Way of Dog – Most Magnificent: The thing that
completes us that beats in our hearts

in our heads
in our blood
in our bones is …

MyManpup. The Way of Dog is MyManpup.

Family

Hey, Scruffity! How are you doing today, boy? I was thinking, maybe Jim will let me have you? You could come home with me. Would you like that? Would that be okay?

No amount of pouncing no
                        bouncing no
yipping and
                yapping no
                        twirling no
                        whirling or spinning could ever say
just how much
okay that is.

NOT FAMILY

Hey kid, look sharp, there are more shoe-legs coming.
Why aren't you spinning? What are you doing?
Are you just going to lie there? When there are all
those other cuter younger pups in all those other cages?
No one will ever pick you like that.

Doesn't that FatRat know?
I already have a home to go to.
FatRat, when MyManpup takes me home you can
have all my kibble.
FatRat doesn't even say thank you.

I wonder if FatRat ever wanted a
Family of his own?

THE WAY OF DOG – A DOG IS A MANY BEASTED THING

I am
A Dog Waiting.
I am
A Dog of Cage
A Dog of Towers (row three, level four)
A Dog Watching Door
A Dog Gnawing on Claws on Paws on Cage
Doors When My Teeth Are Sore
                    because I'm also
A Dog Who Is Bored.
A Dog Who Is Hoping and Moping Because
Hoping Can Be a Tiring Thing
A Dog Dreaming in Swells of a World Outside
and
A Dog Waiting Waiting Waiting for MyManpup
to Come Because It's Been Too Long Already …

And when MyManpup does come

                                        but is quiet
his schnuffle all heavy and dark
            when he scuffs up the dirt
                        his hurt filling the Barn
like Clouds swollen
with storm –

I am
A Dog Who Gets It.

MyManpup splashes water in my dry empty bowl
his face scrunched-crunched small
and his tears fall
split-splat-plitter-plat on the
ground.

*We can't play today, Scruff. Jim will be here real soon.
And … he's sending me to some stupid old boarding
school. He doesn't even like me, doesn't even want me,
he only ever pretended coz of Mum.*

And I am
A Dog Cleaning Tears through the Bars of Cage
and
A Dog Licking Fears and Rage Away
because the lick of a Dog can make
everything everything *everything*
okay.
It's okay, MyManpup. I'm here. I'll help you.
That's what we Dogs do.
          And I think that's another
Way of Dog too.

My paw on his palm helps him calm
and we nuzzle our snouts.

It's okay, Scruffity. I'm here. I'll help you.

Then GrowlManJim

stomps in.

THE BIN

GrowlManJim with his
                    big
black
            kicking-boots
            hard boots
                            fast boots
mean boots
            stomping boots
                            stomps on in and he
pulls MyManpup away.
Tells him his job is not to touch

                                    or talk

            or play
with the mutts. And he spits.

Are you still sulking? That school will do you good.
Your mother was always too soft on you. You need to
toughen up
            he growls

                                        and

my growl matches his
                beat
for
            beat.

But GrowlManJim bangs my bars and snarls
Shut it! A dog too big to be picked will be – crrrrrrkkkkkk
        and he runs a thick finger across his thick neck.
*In fact, boy, you can be the one to do it. Tomorrow that
mutt is going in The Bin.*

And I sound-sna—
hang on. Wait. What did he say? Wait. What?
The Bin?
The Bin full of bones
                full of skin
            full of flies
                full of rot and –
That *DeadDogBin*? To put *me* in? Even though
            I'm still
                currently technically very much still

                        living?

FatRat shrugs. *Yeeesh. Sorry, kid. You know, I think I'll
really miss you. So. Are you going to finish that kibble?*

THE WAY OF DOG — BONES KNOW

The MammaDogs say to listen to
The Way of Dog. They say the *Way*
is what wakes me at night
stirring whirring blurring
kicking my legs in schnuffling dreams of what *could* be
        might be
someday be

              won't ever now be
me.

It's what makes me want to taste the Sky
              race the Sky
place the Sky inside me
to drink every Cloud and Raindrop
      waiting
        to

fall.
To feel the hot of the Sun and the
lick of the Wind prickle my skin

                my fur my
           throat
it's that *HOWLOWLOWL* that swells
        burns

             twists
     turns

so I let it *free*
head tipped to the Moon I know is there even
though I've never
wide-eyed it.

We've pawed our trails, tracked our paws, trailed
our tracks across this ancient wild for thousands and
thousands of ages and those ancient memories do not die
                              the MammaDogs whisper.
Listen to your bones! They know! They know!

But my bones have gone real
quiet.

Those MammaDogs keep calling but

                              I've kind of
stopped

listening.

THE POINT OF CATS

She paw-pads to my cage
her fur pushed through the space
her face against my snout
so I can pretend I am

> Out paw-padding about so I
> can pretend I am

like ScratchCat with No Cage to Contain Her
pretend I am Scruffity with No Cage to Contain
Me
Either.
We sleep curled up

> twirled up

> furled up together

and she purrs, *I'm here. I'm here. I'm here.*

TIME'S UP

Flat-feet are coming
step by   step by

                   step by

                                   step

and the drumming of my heart is so loud
                   the howling from my jaws
the trembling of my paws because
I do not do not do not want to –

                              wait –

The schnuffle in the Air is not
GrowlManJim.
The schnuffle in the Air is

MyManpup.
And my bones ache again to be his Family.
Huh. I guess my bones do know
after all.

HOPE

Hope is a night.
Hope is MyManpup in fright the
                    schnuffle of screeching-scared

that seeps and weeps from his skin in waves.

Hope is the click of the old Barn door
the click of
                    my claws on the cold hard floor
of my teeth on the wire
because when I am nervous
I chew.

Hope is the *hush* on MyManpup's lips
the soft cup of his hands
that gentle me up and away from the dark
from the bark of the MammaDogs'
Go! Go! Go!
while the younger pups in the cages scrunch low
knowing it is not their time.

                                    Not this time.

Hope is ScratchCat
        soft eyes blinking slow.
Go. Go. Go.

Hope is FatRat waving his tail.
See ya round, kid. Good luck out there. You'll need it!
And hey, thanks for all the kibble.

Hope is MyManpup
holding me tight
pouched in his arms the
light of the Moon

            that gleaming glowing pulling
         flowing beautifullest brightest light of the
                                 Moon!
touching my fur
filling me full with dreams of

                    tomorrow.

Hope is MyManpup
                stepping
s   l   o   w   i   n   g

                          stopped at the gate

dropped at the gate

looking back to the Barn
his legs and arms shaking the aching of his heart

so strong while lights flash blue behind him and
somewhere

                                    not so farfarfar from
                        here
right into my well-tuned sound-snatching ears
the Wind carries the wail of

                     alarms.

Hope is MyManpup
scrampering back to the Barn
because tonight

                                maybe

it *is* their time
after all.

Fear

MyManpup unlocks every every every cage
and the fear and sad that rages in waves
swirls into a haze of
confuzzled confusion.

GO! Run, dogs! You're free! Get out of here! Go!

But MyManpup's not knowing those
schnuffles growing on the
Wind is the GrowlManJim getting closer and
I spin and spin and spin but MyManpup
keeps going

                 not knowing not knowing not –
and the Barn is full of grrrurf-awwwoufing of
           yap-yip-yapping of

                       snipping and
             snapping of
               trippsing and trapping
                     barking

howling

            snarling and
              growling in

fear.

Closer! Closer! That's GrowlManJim getting closer!!!
That schnuffle on the Wind is hot anger
roaring blood

WHO'S THERE?
COME OUT HERE!
THE POLICE ARE ON
THEIR WAY!

Metal bat

        bashing hard against cages in rage and

MyManpup's fear is leaking

into mine and fear is fear is fear is fear is fear is

fearfearfearfearfearfearfearfearfearfearfearfearfear

fearfearfearfearfearfearfearfearfearfearfearfearfear

fearfearfearfearfearfearfearfearfearfearfearfearfear

fearfearfearfear fearfearfearfearfearfearfearfear

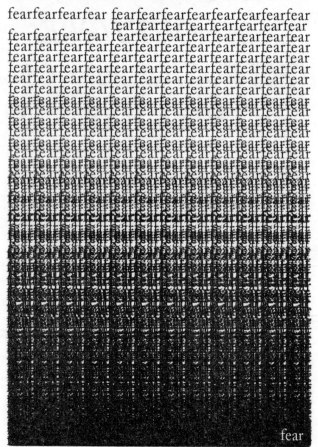

fear

PACK FiERCE

Run! is the call of the MammaDogs
                                free from their cages
                        making a wall
                my pack standing tall before
GrowlManJim.

All of them so thin so

                                                small so
                fierce so
                strong
their growling gnashing snarling hackles raised and
bodies
barring –

Run! The Way of Dog is to Run. Run. RUN!

Free

Free is the tremble of flat-feet coming
chasing
                    racing
hot hurt crashing
                    bashing the ground
while all around the barks and yells swell

                                    then fade ...

The Barn too far now from MyManpup and me
to sound-snatch the cries of my pack standing tall
or to
schnuffle the fates of those who did not
                    make it out
in time.

Sometimes free can feel like

helplessness.

PROMISES

My paws are so sore from padding
through night and all the way
                   through to morning
but MyManpup
     isn't slowing

Come on, Scruff, keep going!

          and with each step he's growing more and more
quiet.
And I am too tired to spin him back to happy.

And when the Sun's first lick on our heads
                   stops us
we curl up tight where the
Tree Roots can nest us and the bright of the
morning
hushes our worrying.

I won't ever leave you. Together forever. I promise.

I promise I promise I promise.

*We aren't ever going back. We'll keep going until we
are so far away he'll never find us. I promise.*

But my brain is still full of that DeadDogBin
                              of GrowlManJim and
in my paw-paddling dreams I scream because
it isn't me that is deep inside
The Bin.
        In my dreams The Bin is full of

                    MyManpup.

FOLLOWING THE RIVER

FiRSTS

Life is SO much more in this Outside-of-Barn world!
There's so much to wide-eye to
         schnuffle and

                              sound-snatch
I want to catch every moment in my mouth and
shake it.

All the tingling on my tongue the
bristling in my fur
         on my skin is filling me up
close to bursting! Is this the way every day is?

Just tasting each trace on the Wind as it passes
rolling in Grasses all full up of Flowers
    schnuffling the tumbling towers of Trees
sound-snatching the whispers that call on the Breeze
        pouncing on Creepers that skattle and skittle
bouncing in each and
                  every little

    puddle

                  again and again and again
chasing the rumblings that roll underground
scrampering and spinning around and around
with happy!

The MammaDogs never told of all *these* wonders!
They never told of holding a sausage on my tongue
or how one comes undone with a schnuffle of bone
or
the crazy race of glee of a ball thrown just for me
or
how a Stick makes teeth feel like
Sunshine.

They never said
how claws scraping Dirt
dark Earth and wet Mud
                    prickles the blood
buzzes through bones
                              brain
                              skin

                                        claw and
                              fur and I'm sure
that To Dig is most definitely a *Way of Dog* too.

I wonder if
those MammaDogs
                    ever even
              knew
the joy of it.

WHYS

MyManpup and me
                we curl up together in
a warm kinda den
with a flustering flock of
                cooing SkySingers
and the day starts to settle

                       and still.

And I want to know
                where does the Sun go?
And what is it that
crawls so far underground
                    I can only sound-snatch
just a whisper
    of digging?

And what is that horrible
                snaking-metal-muncher
                speeding past so fast so close to our
                den?
Why is it hooting and tooting again and again and
why are those shoe-legs stuck inside it?
What happened? Did it eat them?

And why do my paws
                and claws want to scramper

when I look at the Stars when the rest of me's
ready for sleeping?
And what is it that's creeping outside?
What is it that's hiding and
                              prowling and what kind of beast
makes that strange kind of growling?

There is so so so much I want to know!
But MyManpup doesn't seem to
even notice.

THE WAY OF DOG –
FOLLOW YOUR SNOUT

*What are you looking at, Scruffity? Come here. See this
map? I've made a plan. Look. This is where we are going.*

A map? A plan? Who needs a plan for walking this
land?
There's so much right here to discover

uncover and try!
Doesn't he know how the world just flows
how it twirls and unfurls so you don't need to know
just how and just where you are going?
It seems he has no eyes no

snout no
ears for those traces those

snatches
of places you find left behind in
the whispers on Trees

murmurs in Leaves
schnuffles in Grass
or the stories that swell in the prints of those passed.
That's how you find where you're going.
You follow your snout and go with the flow
and it all works out. Doesn't he know?

*We'll go find Aunty Chris. You'll love her. She lives
in this little old wooden house near the beach and the
river flows right past her window. All we've got to do
is follow the river. And then every day we'll go to the
beach, where the sea meets the sky, and we'll lie in the
sand and let the sun warm us through, and we'll swim
in the waves and they'll pick us up and hold us safe
forever.*

And each rub of his hand is a kind of

                         hunger

I can't fill.
Not even when I spin and spin and spin
not even when I lick every bit of his face
or give him my ball to chew and to chase –

                    he just sighs

like a ball can't fix all his troubles.
Doesn't he know *The Way of Dog – A Ball Is All*?

*Chris lived with us before Mum got sick. She'd read me
stories, sing me songs. But then …*

                and I feel his strong tremble and

fade

*But then Mum met Jim and Aunty Chris left and
didn't come back, not even when Mum got sick.
I don't think he let her.*

64

The sad in his eyes is so strong and the
pain in his voice is so loud and the
break in his heart is so huge
I can't lick
                nuzzle
            paw or gnaw
any of that away.

I wish he would
go with the flow so he knows that
no feeling lasts foreverer.

THE WAY OF DOG –
TO HOWL IS TO HEAL

There are some things only fixable by Howl.
The brilliance of a howl is the way that it heals
how it feels in your bones
                              in your chest
              that surging
                                        urging blood
through the rest of your skin
                    releasing
                         everything within
so nothing nothing nothing
keeps you down. We hounds know the secret of living.
MyManpup really needs
to learn to howl.

I start off slow
to show how a howl goes
                    how it tugs
all the sound from waaaaay down low
in your belly.
I nudge-nuzzle with my snout
Come on, MyManpup, let it out! Let it out!

And MyManpup he HOOOOOOWWWWWWLLLLS

Proper Dog.

We'll be all right, won't we, Scruff? I guess it'll all work out, someday.

For that is the brilliance of a howl
of a manpup and his Dog. Together.

Repeated Lessons

I'm growing bigger now
               stronger now
          my jaws snatching harder now
             my paws chasing faster now
             my snout tracking traces now
no treasure can be hidden from me!
So why can't MyManpup see
             the genius in all of my finding?
It's very confusing. Perhaps he just needs some more
showing.

No, Scruffity! What are you doing? Get out of there!

MyManpup only smiles
at SkySingers that caw
and that call and
             flip-flap-fly through the Sky.
His eyes just grow wide when I
schnuffle around to find those on the ground
that have
decomposed just
a little. Those bundles of wonder that
twitch at my snout
so that all about fades
in the fog of such beauty.

With the gentlest jaws
              I lift the gift from the Skies.
Here you go! It's for you, MyManpup! It's for you!
It's for you!
No! Drop that dead crow! It's full of maggots!

And he won't even look
                    he won't even stay
when I show him the way to
                    roll in her
for luck.

Ewww! Don't come near me! You stink!

Doesn't he know that to
                    roll in each schnuffle you find
so it stays in your mind
so you can keep dreaming its living
is *The Way of Dog*?

I think there must be
                    is definitely
something wrong with his snout.

If MyManpup is going to learn about rolling
I'll need to work hard and keep showing him the way.
That's okay.
We Dogs are very patient.

Love is

Love is
sitting with MyManpup
on the Grass in the Sun.

Love is
heads together
                    eyes closed
schnuffling deep.

Love is
a kind of fierce
that aches.

RED RiP WRAP

*Okay, Scruffity. We're heading into a town. We won't
stay long, but while we're here, you need to keep close.
Otherwise people will think you're lost or a stray and
they'll call the ranger on us.*

And MyManpup shuffles his feet
                    his hands rub together
and the beat in his step is all wrong.
I don't think MyManpup likes this town thing much.

Wait. I know!
And he rips a strip of his shirt and he
                    wraps it around my neck.
*There! That should do it. Now people will know that
you and me are a team. They won't take you away
with this on. Whaddya reckon?*

And it is the most amazing thing –
the RedRipWrap schnuffles just like
MyManpup
                    so even when I'm not with him
he is still with me.
I don't even need to roll in him first.

TOWN FEAR

MyManpup tells me not to worry
with all the shoe-legs that are here
but why is he
               in such a hurry and
                         why does he schnuffle
all over of sour
           itching
    fear?
It makes me a little bit
nervous …

And his scared and his sad
soak our skin.

BEAMING LIKE STARS

MyManpup puts his hat on the ground
his arm wrapped around me

               my head on his knee

and we

     w

        a

           i

              t.

         I try not to shake
         when the cold hard ground makes me
         think of the Barn.

And when shoe-legs pass by they're
sometimes looking
         sometimes sighing
heads shaking or whisper-whying but
         sometimes
smiling
         sometimes
flying coins in the hat so MyManpup smiles back.
But this waiting is making me nervous and
         I can't stop my trembling.

*What's wrong, Scruff? Are you cold? We just need
enough money for some food. Hey, Scruffy, let's show
them how clever you are.*
MyManpup tries to put his hat in my jaw.
Carry it, Scruffity. Like you carry your ball!

**No thanks. Can we go? I don't like the way they're
wide-eyeing me. I don't think I like this town thing
much.**

Please, Scruff? Can you do this for me? Please, fella?

And why do his eyes so
                        big so sad so wide
ache me inside and pull my heart into
taking that hat in my jaw?
Good boy, Scruff!

> *Hey, Dad! Dad! Look! That dog
> wants us to give him some money!
> He's holding the hat! He's so smart!
> Can I pat him? Can I?*

And slowly
                                    I stop shaking
and slowly
                                    I stop quaking

and MyManpup pats my back and I
drop the hat and yap and
everyone laughs and
everyone claps and I spin and spin and spin
and that hat fills faster than a hole dug in the Rain.

MyManpup he
beams like the Stars
with his happy.
I guess this town's not so bad after all.

TOWN QUESTIONS

It seems to me that where there
are no Trees
there are lampposts instead and each one
holds a million messages!

I could spend all day making my way
from post to post to post
where each schnuffle says the most
amazing things
        says who has been where and
what is still out there
        to be found. My snout is sore from
so much rubbing on the ground
but everything in this town is just so new and so
curious.

And there are so many Dogs
      behind fences
   and at parks
I want to yip-yap with them all!

And I want to know why
TownDogs tie their shoe-legs to
ropes just to lead them along the street.
Is it to make their shoe-legs go faster?

*Don't worry, Scruff, we won't stick around long. Just a
day or so. Just so we can make some more money.*

Who's worried? These posts are the best! Did
you know that eight Dogs have passed here this
morning? Eight!

And a Dog could dig for hours in the gardens with
the Flowers where snoutfuls of treasure
are all hidden. But here in this town
    I think maybe it's

                    forbidden
because when I do
the Town shoe-legs all yell
and tell us to go
but don't they know that *The Way of Dog is to Dig?*

MyManpup
he gets it.
*Don't worry, Scruff. You weren't to know they were
prize-winning roses. Come on. Just one more day and
then we'll get out of here.*

WHEELS

Why does a shoe-legs whizzing by
on two spinning wheels
make me feel a desperate need to
                        match their speed to
chase them down
                race them down
                                hold them down
when all around horns are honking and shoe-legs
are yelling and swelling with anger
and MyManpup's shouting *NO* and
those shoe-legs are shouting *NO*
and the Dogs behind fences are yapping *NO! NO! NO!*
when I *know*
that shoe-legs are never meant
for chasing?

While my teeth stop
those wheels from spinning around
MyManpup helps the shoe-legs from the ground.
I'm so sorry! Are you okay?

> *Is that your dog? Put it on a
> lead! If you can't control it, you
> shouldn't be allowed to keep it.*

He's still a pup, sort of. He doesn't know any better.
I'm really sorry …

And I'm really truly sorry too. It's just that
the rubber spinning around and around and
the sound-snatching of bells
excite me beyond all
reason.
But I never ever *everer* bite
their legs. Just those wheels that feel so good
in my teeth when
I squeeze them.

> *Look what he's done! Your*
> *bloody dog's popped my tyre!*
> *What's your name? I'm calling*
> *the ranger!*

Come on, Scruffity, let's get outta here.

Can I take this wheel with me? For later? No? Oh.
Okay.

THE SNAKINGMETALMUNCHER

Scruff! I've just had the best idea ever!

MyManpup is skipping and jumping
his arms and legs pumping
and his thrilling is making me
spin.

*With all this money you made us, we don't have to
walk the whole way after all! We'll catch the train!
We'll be there by night-time! Why didn't I think of this
before? Here, wait while I buy us some tickets.*

But I'm not so sure about this …
The schnuffles in this place are so strong
they are making the hairs in my
snout burn.

All right now. Stay close. The train will be here real soon.

But I don't like it here with
all these shoe-legs here
and all their
tap tap tapping here on the ground all
together
squishing and pushing and squashing and mushing
and stepping on my paws

and my jaws can't stop my whining
and I can't stop this feeling this
shivering-shaking that's making
the fur on my back stand tall
and making me feel so very very very small and so
very very very very
frightened.

And now there's a rumbling that's coming
                                        a tumbling that
I think I might know
and it's growing and growing and growing
and it can't be
it's not
*IT IS! IT'S THE MUNCHER! THE
SNAKINGMETALMUNCHER! IT'S COMING
TO EAT US AND CRUNCH US TO SPIT US
UP AND SMUNCH US AND WHAT ARE
YOU DOING, MYMANPUP? WHY ARE YOU
HOLDING ME? WE NEED TO RUN RUN RUN
RUN RUN RUN RUN RUN RUN RUN RUN
RUN RUN RUN RUN RUN RUN!*

*Scruffity! Scruffity! It's okay! It's just a train! Come
on! Trust me!*

*WHAT IS WRONG WITH YOU? DO YOU WANT
TO GET SMUNCHED? DON'T YOU KNOW*

ANYTHING? NO NO NO NO NO NOOOO!
DON'T GO NEAR THAT THING!!!

And MyManpup slumps on the ground
            wraps his arms tight around me and he
shhhhhhhes me to

                                            quiet

while the Muncher
            moves slowly away.

It's okay. I guess we'll just walk. We'll follow the river, like
we said. Who wants to go on a stupid old train anyway?

It takes a long time for my shaking
to still.

STORM

Why do I have this strange kind of feeling?
My skin is all prickling

                my hackles stand tall like I'm
falling. Like
we should be running.
Like
a strange kind of Storm is

                coming.

Why do I have this

                strange
            kind of

                    feeling?
My skin is prickling

            my hackles stand tall like I'm
f
a
l
l
i
n
g.

Like we should be running.

Like
a

strange
kind of
Storm
is

coming.

JUST A STICK

MyManpup collects Sticks

                  his tongue poked through his lips

and he pecks those Sticks with his knife into

'treasures'.

Look, Scruffity, I've made a dragon!

But he doesn't let me take them and

                  chew them to improve them

just a bit.

*No, Scruff! You'll ruin it! We'll leave it here for someone
to find.*

And he keeps making and

taking *my* Sticks that

I'm saving for chewing.

How's that work?

Look, Scruffity, I've made a bird!

It's a Stick.

I've made a frog!

It's a Stick.

I've made a fish!

**Still a Stick. It schnuffles nothing like a
SwishRiverFish. What's wrong with your snout?**

86

I've carved a dog! Here, I'll put an S on it for
Scruffity.
That's a Dog? Really?
It's for you.
To chew? Oh. No? Are you sure? Well then.

MyManpup ties the 'Dog' on my RedRipWrap
with string.
So you don't ever forget who you are, Scruff.

I lick his hands and face
but I don't need to place some
knife-bitten Tree around my neck
to remind me who to be.
I am MyManpup's Scruffity
forever and everer and
always will be.

It's like the star Mum carved for me.

I schnuffle his thing on the string round his neck and
taste the trace of soft hands and of
loving.

She said the stars shining in the sky are those we love
who are gone looking down on us, so we know we are
never alone.

And I place my paws on his hands
so MyManpup understands
that he isn't ever alone
                even without
those Stars shining.

THE WAY OF DOG –
RULE MOST IMPORTANT

The Way of Dog
is to keep our shoe-legs safe.

Shoe-leg brains are unaware of all the
danger that is there
                    their snouts just can't catch
those warnings in the Air all around us.

I thought I knew
what to do.
But then that strange kind of Storm
comes crashing

down.

BREAKiNG THE WAY OF DOG

MyManpup is calling
Come on, Scruffity, let's go!

But I'm chasing a Rabbit and am
too slow. Too

        slow.
***Yeah, yeah, I'm coming! Just a minute. Just a sec. This
Rabbit is somewhere real close. Can you schnuffle her?
Can you? Can you?***

But he's standing on the
road
        MyManpup.

He's waiting
on the
road
        MyManpup.
*Come on, Scruffity! Hey! Do you know what today is?
It's your birthday! This calls for a real special breakfast!*

And suddenly I'm

                feeling the rumblings
          the tumblings of
          MetalBeasts that feast on

creatures that wait on
                    roads and ***Run! MyManpup! Run!***

That MetalBeast comes so fast
the horn blasting a warning too

            late

that MetalBeast smashing
                            crashing
            MyManpup
who is only made of skin and bones so easily

broken.

Manpups are not made to flip-flap-fly
through the Sky they
have no wings to carry them high and keep them
safe.
And my barks do nothing
to soften his
fall.

The MetalBeast keeps going
                            not slowing
for the screams of a Dog
                            not slowing
for a manpup

broken and twisted in ways a manpup should
never twist.

And his blood
falls warm from his head
onto mine.

MyManpup?

PROMISE

He schnuffles like
the deepest dark
Earth
and his
breath

        brain
     being
are
all

      slowing.

     Going.

We are forever forever foreverer together, remember?
I promise, I promise, I promise, remember? Be strong,
be fierce, be strong, be fierce be be

Lick

       nuzzle
  bark
      howl
    try to make him

                    wake
but
  my paws
                    teeth
                              claws can't stop the shaking of his
                    breathing
gush of blood
                    ache of bones
                              body turning stone
                                        h
                                          e

                                            a
                                               v

                                               y

        and his heart is
beating so hard
                    out
        of
                    time.

I tell him with my eyes
                              tongue
        snout
every bark
        yelp
              yowl every
grunt every growl and *HOWOWOWL*
    BE STRONG, BE FIERCE, THERE IS MORE!

And a bigger MetalBeast
                lights all flashing beaming glowing sirens
                                        screaming loudly
                        growing
                hands grabbing
                                holding and
there are too many and
Together foreverer promise promise foreverer
when hands all unknown try to grab him I
        get in their way so MyManpup and me can stay
together together together him and me we
are a We
and his RedRipWrap
                on my neck protects me
from those who think I'm only a Me …
but
                                it's not me
they are wanting.
I should have
hung a DogRipWrap around
                MyManpup.

                        Together foreverer

and they push me away from MyManpup they
hold me they
                tell me to stay away from MyManpup
then they take him away.
                MyManpup.

WOLF FAST

They put MyManpup in that
FlashingMetalBeast

and I don't know what to
I don't know where

how
I don't
HOWOOOWOOOOWWWLLLLLLLLLLLLLL
and why why why
HOWOOOWOOOOWWWHOWWWWLLLLLL
and nothing
stills my mind to knowing
what to do. How do I get you
out
MyManpup?

And now the FlashingMetalBeast is moving away and
the pain in my head
in my bones in
my heart is tearing
and gnawing and scratching me apart and
I don't know what to do I
don't know where—

Dogs are not supposed to be so
scared.

All I know is MyManpup
needs me. Together. Forever. Foreverer.
All I know is nothing can keep us
apart.
No MetalBeast can ever be
as fast as a Dog chasing to get
his manpup free.
And my paws pad faster
my blood beats harder
my legs and fur all scream and stir me into
scrampering Wolf fast and
                    fierce along that road
chasing
      racing to catch
that MetalBeast.

*I'm coming, MyManpup! Don't go! I'm coming! I'm
coming! I'm—*

too

                    slow.

BIG
CITY

—

TRACKS

Listen to The Way of Dog. Your bones know. Listen.
Listen. Listen.
So I listen. So I remember.
So just because I was too slow
to catch that FlashingMetalBeast
doesn't mean I don't know
where to go to find it.
That is *The Way of Dog – Follow Your Snout.*
And even though a snoutful of tyre is
hard to track
when the road is covered is
smothered in trails in

                       tracings
            twirling through my head in

a storm
I will not ever
stop.

That FlashingMetalBeast left its own kind of trace
a schnuffle of places it's been
and maybe
just maybe
that is where it is going.
I'm coming, MyManpup. I'm coming.

PADDING NIGHTWARD

Why is it that a Dog
paw-padding his way through day towards night and
deep deep deep into
morning
makes shoe-legs blare their warning and yell
while their MetalBeasts leave snakey
                    swervey tracks in black all over
the road? Why can't they slow and
watch where they're going?
Don't they know I can't trail a trace
if my snout isn't placed low to the ground?
Don't they know the sound-snatching
of words hurled through the Air is distracting?

Don't they know what
can happen when they do not
pay attention?

Sometimes I
just don't understand
The Way of Shoe-Legs
at all.

Licking

Sometimes even a lick lick lick
cannot unstick the blood that drips from paws.
Roads should be made of
softer stuff.

TRAIL ENDS

The *Way of Dog* does not say where to go
when my snout
doesn't know which trail to follow.
It led me here where there are
more MetalBeasts on roads
than Stars in the Skies
and each concrete den and pen
is filled with hundreds of
shoe-legs. How am I to know
which one is holding
MyManpup?

I think I'm in a place they call
BigCity.

BigCity Learnings

Things are so so so different in BigCity.
And everything is so so so loud.
The Stars are all faded and faint
        the River is tainted and schnuffles all wrong
the smoke and the fug in the Air is so
strong it burns
                in my snout.
I don't think BigCity is for me.

And BigCity shoe-legs all hurry
                        flurry
                    scurry
            turn angry and mad
and yell that I'm bad
when I look for food in their bins.
                        And why is it wrong
to take meat from a table or
bread from a bag
if my tail is wagging in thanks? Don't they know I
am hungry?
Can't they schnuffle my scared when I bare
my tummy or hold my head low
to the ground?
Doesn't the sound of my crying
tell them why I am here?

Where are you, MyManpup? Where are you?

And where is the Grass? The Dirt? The Flowers?
There are no tumbling towers of Trees or
swarms of brrrumbling
                                        Bees all singing their song.
Just long long long stretches of concrete.
Don't they know life is more?

And why do BigCityDogs
never slow when I ask where to go
                                        don't stay to yip-yap
        just paw-pad away
with their snouts in the Air
like they don't even care
        like they can't even sound-snatch my asking.
When all I'm asking is
***Have you seen MyManpup? Have you? Have you
seen MyManpup?***

So even though that River schnuffles all wrong
                                        the heavy in my belly is so so strong
        my paws pad me along those streets to
her edge. Somewhere in that Water there
are the same drips
                        the same drops that cleaned
                                        that cooled MyManpup and me that

held us up that flowed and towed us
that whispered *Follow me. Follow me.*
Follow me.
So even though the fug in the Sky
is so thick the Moon's bright cannot
even reach me I
tip my head to that Sky and I howl
out all of my fears and
aloneness.

Where are you, MyManpup? Where are you?
Where are you?

BiGCiTy Fox

There's a bark like a scream
in the dark and it echoes across
the River.
And a schnuffle of fur that tastes of
the blurring and stirring of
             Storms and of Forests

                                    so soft and so
light I think maybe I might have just
dreamed it.
But there he is
Small Scrappy Skinny Patchy BigCity Fox
on the bank of the River
                    in the shadow of not yet morning

his eyes closing soft
in a Fox kind of greeting.

*Hey there, friend. Looks like you're
new in town. I bet you must be
reeeeaaal hungry. What's your
name? Where you from? What's
wrong — don't you know how to
speak*

                    Fox?

Following Fox

Sometimes an old ribbed PatchFox
with clumps of fur missing and scars on his face
might just be

what a lost confused Dog like me
needs.

**Can you help me? I need to know where to find a
FlashingMetalBeast with lights all beaming and
sirens screaming and—**
What you want one of them for?
I'm looking for MyManpup.
*Ohhhhh. That's why you're wearing that thing 'round
your neck. Well sure. I can show you where to go, but
first, let's get us a feed. You need to keep your strength up
'round here, you know. The weak ones don't last long …*
You can show me where to go?
Of course. I'm a Fox.

And just like that he's off.
And just like that

I follow.

And this PatchFox sure seems to know
exactly where he is going.
We paw-pad over and up and around
we pick through the bin-bits all blown on the ground

                we go over the ridge and under the
bridge
and down
 down
        down
through the drains underground
that schnuffle of Rain and of journeying.

Come on, friend, we're almost there.
Where?
*You'll see. Trust me. You'll love it. But quick now, we
need to get there while the Sun is still waking.*

And there's a schnuffle in the Air now of –
what is that?
Is that really
could it truly be
                my favourite treat?
Is it *meat*?

And I think an old PatchFox
is definitely just what
                a lost confused Dog like me
needs.

DiVERSiON

So, friend, did anyone ever teach you how to be
A Diversion?
A di-what-sion?

It is very hard to concentrate
with the schnuffle of meat
so strong in the Air and my
tongue all preparing to taste it.

Quit drooling on my fur! A Diversion. A Distraction.
The main attraction of the show. You are gonna be
perfect. You see, I've been weavin' a scheme in my
superior Fox-smart brain and I've been waitin' a long
time to try it out. See that butcher shop just there?

How could I miss it!
The one with the meat of every kind all lined up in
the window?
That's the one. But that shop is full of shoe-legs with
their knives and boots and legs that kick at anyone they
aren't fond of. And those shoe-legs are so suspicious of us
Foxes. Go figure. But I reckon, with your cute puppy-
dog eyes, you're exactly what my plan's been needin'.
We just have to wait for those bells to sound coz that's
when they open their door. And that's when we can be
sure that they'll see you.

What bells?
The seven bells of the shoe-leg morning, of course.
I guess their snouts and eyes aren't as wise to the Sun as
ours. Wait for it … there!

Wow. That PatchFox sure is clever.
How did he know those bells would go?
And how did he know those
shoe-legs would open their door?

Now remember, be LOUD. And don't run away 'til I
tell you.
Wait. What?

Then PatchFox rubs his snout
on my favourite paw and opens up his jaw
                        with a wide foxy grin and

        s
        i
        n
        k
        s
his teeth in.

OW

I yowl.

Fox Smarts

That PatchFox is real smart

                      if not just a little bit
sneaky.
Those shoe-legs from the shop come running
their hands on my head patting
voices cooing

                wooing
Awwww, look at this poor dog! What happened?
Come here, pup-pup. Let me have a look at you.

And while they're all happy-helping me
they don't even see
that PatchFox creep inside

                    not even trying to hide and
he's munching and crunching on meats and
treats and with his teeth he grabbles up
a whole long string of
sausages.

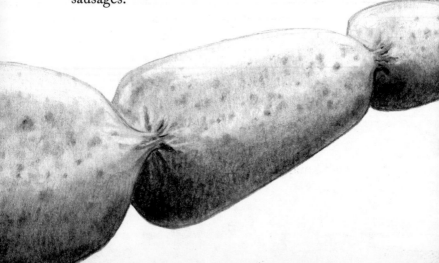

*Hey! Is that that bloody fox again?! In my shop?! Get
out of there!*

And then those knives and boots and kicking legs
appear—

> *We're done here!*
>> PatchFox scrampers out the door
> *Come on, friend! Run! Run! Run!*

Easier said than done

                    when your favourite paw

is still throbbing.

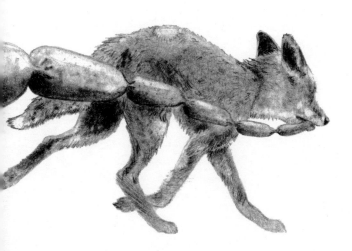

MEAT IS MY FAVOURITE TREAT BUT ...

I'm not so sure
the pain in my paw
was worth just three sausages taken
from a string of eight.
But a Fox Always Keeps His Word.

All right, friend. Let's go find your manpup.

THE FIXINGDEN

PatchFox leads me back through the streets
to where the FlashingMetalBeasts meet and

there's a strange kind of edge to the Air
here.
A strange kind of quiet a

still
even though everyone's
moving. It's like a strange kind of
scary kind of
waiting.

See in there? That's where they take the shoe-legs when
they're hurt or are real sick. It's a den where they fix
them, if they can fix them. But sometimes, you know,
friend, nothing can be done. Maybe it was his time to—
Where? In there? Come on, then! Let's go!

And PatchFox barks *NO* but if MyManpup is
there
then that is where I
need to be.

I race across the road
through the flashing and the legs

through doors that swoosh-woosh me

                                    into a place
where the ground on my paws
is so slippery my claws can't grab hold
and I'm skittering

                    scattering
claws clip-clattering

                        my jaws yip-yappering in
confuzzled surprise and I
wide-eye those shoe-legs
charging ...

                        Get that dog out of here!
MyManpup! Are you here? Are you here? Are you—

But hands hard and rough
grab my fur grab

                    my scruff and hurl me
back out through those swoosh-woosh doors.
I crawl back to PatchFox
on my belly.

So. How did that go for you, friend?
I don't know if MyManpup is there. It schnuffled all
wrong and pawed all wrong and the sour in the Air
was so strong—
You need to learn Fox Waiting. Be patient. Be still.
Be invisible. Choose your moment wisely, my friend.

Sometimes things take time. And who knows, maybe he's not in the FixingDen. He could be at the square where all those shoe-legs gather. It's just down there. Or maybe he's on his way to the Sea – you said that's where you were going.

The Sea? Would MyManpup go to the Sea
without me?

What I mean is, maybe that's where he thinks you will be.
PatchFox nuzzles my snout.
Don't give up, friend. Who knows what is waiting on the other side of morning. But I need to go now. The Sun is out and shining bright. We Foxes don't do well in the light of the day. Are you going to stay? If you are, make sure you keep your eyes wide for those Rangers. They come with their wire sticks that loop round your neck and they scoop you right up and take you away in their Van. And no one ever comes back from The Van. So be careful, okay?
But I'm not a stray. I have my RedRipWrap, remember?
Hmm. Well, friend, thanks for helping with my plan. I hope you find your manpup.

And just like that
he is gone.

The Way of Dog — Keep Chasing

The square. The square. That's
where MyManpup will be
waiting just for me.
I'm sure of it. I'm sure of it. I'm

                                 not

sure of it at all.
But I have to
keep chasing

               keep racing
so the fear
doesn't chew me up
whole.

And that PatchFox is right. The square is where
all those shoe-legs go to throw crumbs in the Air
for the SkySingers to share. But
where is MyManpup?

I stay all day

                    all night
scrunched tight behind bins
the cold of my skin shivering

                   quivering my bones
be patient, be still, be invisible
         who knows what is waiting
     on the other side of morning

and I can pretend this corner's my den
and I can pretend I will be here when
MyManpup flat-foots past.
And I can pretend the rough of the ground
the cold of the ground is nothing at all
like the Barn.

But even though I stay
                                        another night
                        another
            day
wide-eyeing every one going by
            be patient, be still, be invisible
                        who knows what is waiting
            on the other side of morning
there is still no sign
of MyManpup.

But there will be. I'm sure. I'm sure.
I'm
Fox Waiting
even though I'm a Dog.

121

Curious

It seems I'm not the only one Fox Waiting
in this square for their
someone.
There's an old shoe-legs that's hunched
with a sad all over ache and her bones all over
creaking and shaking.
And she doesn't say a word but she schnuffles of
stones and
of roads and of

waiting.

She wide-eyes me and I wonder
just what
she is thinking.

Sharing Breakfast

Sometimes no words are needed
when chips are offered from
cold half-gloved hands in the quiet
of morning.

We decide to wait for our someones
together.
It's warmer that way.

This Old Trick

The OldOne is kneeling
with her hat on the ground and all around her
other shoe-legs are
sometimes looking
        sometimes sighing
heads shaking or
whisper-whying but
        not ever sometimes
smiling
        not ever sometimes
flying coins in the hat so the OldOne smiles back.

But I've seen this trick before.
Doesn't she know
        she's not doing it right?

Spinning MyManpup Close

Sometimes shoe-legs need
a nudge in the right direction
       from a Dog
           taught with perfection
to get money and applause
from a hat held in the jaws.

And the taste of that hat
flies me back to being
       just me and MyManpup.
           When everything everything
         everything was okay.

And even though I don't know
         what to do or where to go
even though I am full up of fear
and MyManpup isn't here
I spin spin spin
and I feel MyManpup near –
because spinning always
       brings happiness.

And the faster I spin the more shoe-legs smile
the more they go completely wild.
I guess shoe-legs know the power of a spin.

And I see just a hint
of Stars beaming in
OldOne.

STRING THING

In the night when all the lights
in all those dens turn to dark
and the shoe-legs in the streets
have gone away
and there are no wide-eyes watching and
no ears sound-snatching then
OldOne gets her StringThing and she

                        slowly

          softly

            quietly

starts to play.
And the songs that
StringThing plays
bloom knowings in
my brain

filled with fear and loud bangs
                    with fiery Rain that
fall in Waves
                    all around us.
Songs that tell of OldOne's pain and
                    the strain of her heart
from being so far apart from her family
            the never knowing where they are or
when she will see them
again.
If she will see them
                                        again.

Songs that tell of the sinking of a boat
of people floating in the Water.
Waves too big too
            dark to see past.
Thunder too loud to cry for help.
So all she has left to hold onto now
is hope and a
            StringThing to tell her song
to a Dog who knows
how to listen.

MISTAKEN

I wake and for a moment I can
schnuffle MyManpup on the Wind.
It's him! It's him! MyManpup! It's him!
But there's no one here

        but OldOne.

I must have been dreaming.
OldOne strokes my fur and I guess I
        just have to wait a little longer.
But I wonder –
does this mean MyManpup is
still close?

The Way of Shoe-Legs

An even better trick than
Dog Spins with Hat in Jaws
is Dog Walks Tall on Hind Paws
and Dog Walks and Talks in Barks
that have no meaning at all.
That gets a lot of smiles a lot

       of pats

a lot of money tossed in hats
a lot more people

    coming close

     Are you here, MyManpup? Are you?

a lot of treats
a lot of laughs

Are you getting that on video? It's amazing!

and I start to understand *The Way of Shoe-Legs* –
They think it's great when
Dogs Pretend at Being Them.
But I reckon
they'd be better off
Pretending at Being Dog.
They might learn something.

SCHNUFFLES

OldOne schnuffles all wrong.
There's a twitching in my snout
that shouts of something creeping
                something growing and slowing her
        down
a tremble of blood
a collection of germs in a wound so old
it escapes detection while
                the infection grows stronger
the longer it blooms.

There's no arguing with
this *Way of Dog – The Snout Knows*
Everything.

THEY NEVER LISTEN

If only shoe-legs knew how a
lick from a Dog could take sickness away
how we heal ourselves every every every day
all the time from the
grime the world sneaks inside us.

If only shoe-legs knew to
                        listen to Dogs because
we Dogs are excellent helpers.
It's one of our *Ways*.

But OldOne just won't listen.
OldOne won't be licked or herded by soft nips
out of the square and into the street
where those FlashingMetalBeasts meet.
She won't let me lead her and guide her
inside that FixingDen and I guess
not all shoe-legs are quite
so easy to train. Some of them
are really quite
stubborn.

HELP

When in the morning OldOne won't wake
when even a shake of her arm in my jaws won't make
her eyes

        open

when those shoe-legs all pass by and don't
stop to wide-eye if she's even

                  okay

and her
breath
          brain
            being
are
all

              slowing ...

This cannot cannot *cannot* happen
again.
But now I know just
where to go for help.

CATCHING ATTENTION

With OldOne's hat in my jaws
I scramper.
Out of the square and into the street
back to where the FlashingMetalBeasts meet
through the doors that swoosh-woosh me right
into that slippery ground den.

Is that that dog again? Get him OUT!

But this time I am ready. This time I am
steady so my paws don't scatter and my claws
don't clatter
                        so much.
I have learned what it takes
to catch those shoe-legs'
attention.

A Dog walking tall on hind paws
with a hat in his jaws
grrrrphing and spinning back out through
those doors
spinning and grrrrphing and walking up tall
                                        so all of them stop and
watch and
wonder.

What's he doing?
            Where did he come from?
Do you think he is trying to show us something?

And other shoe-legs are laughing
wide-eyeing and pointing.

            Are you filming this? Look at him go!

And one of them bends so her face is down low
            her hand on my head and I
                  know
that this shoe-leg speaks Dog.
I let the hat fall
            take her hand
      in my jaw
            Okay, I'm coming
and I paw-pad her
            paw-pad them all
back to the square.

There she is. See? See? See? Can you fix her? Can you?
Clever dog! Everyone, stay back! I'm a doctor!

And this time I don't try to
            stop those Flashing MetalBeasts.
This time I know just what to do
                  just where to go and

how to be so she can still be with me.
I have taken that fear in my jaws
and shaken it
free.

A WONDER

And they agree I am amazing
that without any teaching without any training
I did what I did but
                    still
              they turn me away
                    still
they say I can't stay in the FixingDen
                              even though the nearness of a
Dog makes everyone and everything
better (*The Way of Dog – Be Near*).

*Hospitals are no places for dogs. But you know, you
really are A Wonder.*

If nothing else I guess
these shoe-legs are good judges
of character.

WAITING

Just because a door is closed
                    doesn't mean I can't wait outside
and just because I need to hide whenever that
                                        Ranger
in The Van goes by
and just because I get wooed away by
schnuffles of food or the whirr
of something curious stirring the Wind
Is that you, MyManpup? Oh. No. Mistaken again.
                    doesn't mean I won't be back
to wait some more.
Just to make sure OldOne is okay because
just because someone goes away in a
FlashingMetalBeast
doesn't mean they won't ever
come back.

                                Does it?

I just need to wait for her just
a little bit
longer.

Famous

Hey, Mum! Look! There's WonderDog! That's him,
isn't it?

What's WonderDog?

You know! #WonderDog! That video of the busking
dog who led doctors to the dying woman! He is proper
famous! It was on the news and everything. And that's
him! Is he still waiting for her, do you think?

    Poor thing. Here, pup. Are you hungry? Do you
    want this sandwich?

I yip-yap and spin and walk tall on my paws
and the shoe-legs give me more and more
treats. They really are so easy to train.

A Song Just For Me

OldOne is better! Better! Better!
She walks out those doors
              kisses my paws with promises of a day
when everything will be okay
                                        after all.

A man takes her arm in his hand.
Thank you
he whispers and strokes soft my fur
*thank you for helping my sister. I saw you dancing in
those videos. I saw how you helped her. Without you,
I never would have found her. We thought you could
come home with us?*

And OldOne beams with all the
happiness in the world.
I put my paw on OldOne's hand
                              so she understands
                    so she knows it is my time to go
to follow that River to find
MyManpup. I won't find him around here anymore.
Goodbye, OldOne.

OldOne nods and kisses me goodbye
and although it isn't night
and OldOne isn't out of sight

out of sound of the world all around her
she takes out her StringThing and she
slowly
softly
quietly
starts to play.
And the song that StringThing plays
is a song just for me and it swells in my head

a River and a Sea and it

blossoms a Someday
of MyManpup and me
together.

BiGCiTyDoGS

My thinkings are so full of Somedays
                              of Rivers and of Seas
of MyManpup and me that I don't even see
I'm heading their way
until it's

                                                                    too
                                                      late.

Hmmm. Mmmm. Mmm. What have we have we
have we here?
                    Looks like we've new fur on our patch …

Oh. Not all Dogs are like me.
Not all can see that
a Dog paw-padding along
in the warm of the evening
isn't doing any wrong
isn't doing any harm
is no cause for alarm and should just be left
to continue his journey.

There are eight BigCityDogs and I try
to stop my bones from shaking
but all I can schnuffle in the Air are clouds of
my own scared.

Hey, you! What you doin' on our ground?

On our patch!

*Are you refusin' to respect us? You expect us to just let
you be?*

You reckon we just let you be?

Nawww. You need to answer to The Pack.

I don't look in those BigCityDog eyes
because their eyes tell only of danger.
I don't look at those BigCityDog tails
because the wail that's inside me is
threatening to spill and this Pack
looks like it's waiting to—

I don't want to think about it.

I flatten down low and whimple-whine soft and slow
rolled over on my back so they know

I mean no harm and I tell them
of MyManpup and of where I am going.

*A manpup? All he cares about is owning – that's why
he tied that thing to your neck so's you get fooled into
respecting him.*

*Take it from us. We know a
thing or two about The Way of
Shoe-Legs. They ain't worth drool.*

Dogs is just a toy for them to play with.

Then they get bored and throw us away.

Look at us here. Thrown out, grown out, kicked out,
neglected. You don't expect your manpup to be different,
do you, Dog?

And those BigCityDogs are circling.
Those BigCityDog teeth are bared
and I'm not strong
I'm not fierce
I'm just really truly bone-shaking
                        leg-quaking
      breath-breaking
scared.

And now I'm pinned on my back on the ground
while the
            Pack moves around and around and around
and their Leader with his paws on my chest
with his jaw dripping drool on my snout
is growling from

                  deep
                  down
                  in
                  his

                  gut.

Let me rip that rag from your neck. Give your respect to The Pack. Tell us that for a fact and maybe we might let you join us.

It depends on how good you fight …
Well? What'll it be, Dog? That manpup or us?

I think of MyManpup. And I wait for
the Pack to destroy me.

JUST WHAT A LOST CONFUSED DOG LIKE ME NEEDS

*Hey, friend! We meet again! How's the paw? Looks
like you got yourself into a bit of bother. Never mind,
these mutts are softer than butter. Easy to outfox.
What's the matter, mutts? What's wrong – don't you
know how to speak*

Fox?

AGAINST THE ODDS

Is it true that an old PatchFox
with clumps of fur missing
                            barking and hissing
            sharp teeth biting
fierce strong fighting can be enough
                                            all on his
                                    own
to hold off a blood-thirsting
                            full-grown
pack of BigCityDogs?

Run, friend! Run!

I hope so.
I hope so.

LEADER OF THE PACK

The Leader of The Pack is
not fooled by a patchy old Fox
who has decided to be
a diversion

                a distraction

                the main attraction

for a Pack who just wants something

        furry

to attack.

The Leader of the Pack

                    is after

me.

NO ESCAPE

The Leader of The Pack is
coming for me and he's
faster on his paws than me
                      his jaws are getting close to me and
I run over the ridge and onto the bridge
and the River is raging beneath me
and I see

                                        too late

that I have made a
big mistake.
                      Because

the Leader of The Pack is
frothing with his fierce
with his fur ripping
            blood-thirsting anger
and I can't outrun him
any longer. And up here on this bridge there's
nowhere to go.
Nowhere but …

I guess I wanted to follow the River
after all.

And so I

L
E
A
P.

OH

They say Cats have nine lives.
What I'd like to know
          as I tumble through the Sky
is how many lives do they say
a Dog has?

ANOTHER KIND OF CONCRETE FLOOR

Every time I've swum before
the Water has been real
          soft.
But when my body hits this River
                cold hard cracked crumbling
           dark and numbing
it's like falling onto
concrete.

GOING UNDER

Bone Memory tells us Dogs how to swim
                                    we give in to that
            knowing we feel in each limb
as it pushes us through the Water.
But when that River is pushing and pulling
                                    toing and froing
            growing rougher
                tougher
        stronger
and she's holding you longer and
longer under her being
                    crashing
                bashing
you against her rocky floor
                and you wonder how much more of this
your lungs can take before they break wide
open –

            when that happens
Bone Memory goes
                real
quiet.

I wonder
with the River inside me
                    and me inside the River

does this mean I am River too?
And if I am River
            and River is me
then one day I guess
I'll get to the Sea.

I wonder if MyManpup will be
waiting.

            I'm just so very
            very very
so

                        so

t i r e d.

NEW JOURNEYS

—

FLOTSAM

It is hard to wake when your eyes
are crusted with grit and grime and
the slime from the River's so deep
                        in your snout no amount of
                                sneezing
relieves it.

And that cold River wet is in my fur my
                        skin my
blood and the Mud is too thick too
                                strong to
release me. And my bones are too tired
to stand. I just want to keep sleeping.

But my body wakes with a rattling shake and I find
I am nowhere near
BigCity.

All the Trees grown up around me
                        curl their Branches and surround me
in a Forest of Leaves and of
schnuffles. And those Trees are holding
me safe. And the Mud under my paws
is cooling the soreness the
                        ache of every single
part of me.

I'm just going to
                    lie here
sleep here

a
while.

INTERRUPTIONS

And then they come.

Pippa! What's that? Look, Pip! Look!

> *What? It's nothin', Lila May. It's just a dog.*

TAIL BETRAYAL

Just a Dog? I'm *just* a Dog?
I'm not impressed by their tone
or those gripping
                        grabbing hands trying to
make me their own when I'm happy
lying alone by the River.

What's a dirty old dog doing here? He must be lost.

Lost? Don't they know a Dog can go wherever?
And that PippaPip looks at me
                                              real sharp
her face all scrunched and her hands
clunched tight like
Rocks.
And there's a growl in her voice
and a prowl
in the way that she circles.

But the smaller one smiles and
holds out her hand and she schnuffles of Grass and of
sandwich.
            Hi. I'm Lila May. What's your name?

162

And her hand on my ear is
soft-warm and gentle and she offers me
the apple she's been munching.
Oh. Thanks. That's nice. And delicious.
And my tail starts thumping
even though I don't care for these
grabbing

       poking
   prodding

          pulling
yipping-yapping girlpups.
Tails are the hardest
to train.

LilaMay she
   squeals and laughs
   Is he lost? We could have him! Is he ours, Pip?
   Is he ours?

Don't these girlpups know
          they can't own a Dog
without a Dog owning them first?
They need to wait to get chosen.

What do we want with a mangy mutt? He's half
drowned and probably has fleas. He must belong

to someone with that thing around his neck.
And anyway, I don't reckon Uncle Jay would like
a dog much.

I turn away to say
that I agree entirely with this UncleJay
                                        even though my tail
                        keeps thumping.

I stand up to go. So they know I'm not playing.
So they know I'm not staying. I'm
getting all ready to paw-pad away
and follow the River like always.
I'm going. In just a minute.
But LilaMay keeps patting and my
tail keeps wagging and I wonder—

Come on, Lila May. We've got to go.

They flat-foot away
        with LilaMay turning
                with LilaMay waving

                                                to me
as they trot through the Trees.

Oh. Well. Good.
They were far too loud
                proud and

prodding even if
they did schnuffle pretty lovely.
Even if LilaMay's voice was bright and
bubbly like a
Stream.

NO HURRY

I should get going. Back on my way.
For I am a Dog with Things to Be Doing and
Places to Be Going.
But maybe just for one more day
I think I will stay in this place by the River.

I am still so so tired. And I really do like
the schnuffles of the Breeze
and the whisperwash of Trees in this particular
spot.
That's all.
It's not like I'm waiting.

Safe Keeping

My 'Dog' made by MyManpup
from wood chewed by knife
is gone! It's gone! It's GONE!
I've schnuffled all over and it's nowhere to be
found
and I'm never ever never going to find it
and it's gone gone gone gon—
                              Oh!
Here it is.

                    So you don't ever forget
                    who you are, Scruffity …

I dig a hole to bury it safe
                         my claws my
                   paws scraping
                   deep

                         deeper

                         deepest
through those Leaves
                   Dirt and Rock
so I can lock my treasure
in the belly of the ground where

only the best diggers could ever find it.
And I leave my trace around the place
where it waits so I can go and know
it will be here when I come back.

                          But maybe
I should guard it.
Just for one more day.
Just to be safe.

TRUST

They're back! They're back! They're –

                                        not that I care. It's just
                            interesting is all.
And LilaMay squeals
                    claps her arms around my neck
and burbles
You stayed! You waited! Pippa, isn't he the greatest?

And I learn that a Dog
                        without even trying
can sometimes purr
like a Cat.

But PippaPip glares with her head to the side
and she chews on her lip like she's trying to decide
what I'm good for.
        Huh. He's just a dirty old dog.

Don't you listen! LilaMay holds her hands on my ears
even though that can't stop me sound-snatching.
*You're the most beautiful dog in the whole big huge
wide world! Are you hungry?*

And she feeds me her bread and her butter
                            while my chest flutters like a

Moth
and PippaPip mutters
Don't think you're getting any of mine.

I guess PippaPip is not one for sharing.

> *Come on, Lila May, we're not here to fool around
> with some dog. You're supposed to be learning to
> swim.*

And LilaMay stops.
And LilaMay shuffles real close and
                    a schnuffle of fear
washes over her.

> *Uncle Jay says. If you don't, he'll just throw you in,
> and then you'll have to learn to swim or drown
> trying. That ain't fun. Trust me.*

And I try to say with the way my head nudges
It's okay – just go with the flow of the water.
But her body is all over shivery-shaking
                    making her tremble and shrink
so I stand
take her hand in my jaw and paw-pad her down
to the River.
And I schnuffle just a sliver
                    just a wisp of a thought that maybe
            she'd be taught

if it is me
        who is doing the teaching.
She must know
we Dogs are very good teachers.

SWIMMING

Mouth gasping
                    hands grasping
                              clasping tight to my fur
                    to my neck
then slowly
slowly
LilaMay matches the
                    way my legs churn
the way that they turn to keep us afloat and
slowly
                    slowly
LilaMay begins
                    to swiiiiiiiiiim
                              Proper Dog.

HOMECOMING

Hmm

        PippaPip looks real hard at
me her mouth all
            squirled with thinking
*I guess he is sort of clever. For a dog. Do you think we
should try to take him home after all?*

        *That would be the bestest! Would you like
        that? Do you wanna come home with us?*

And LilaMay squeals her hands clutching tight and
        I guess that's okay
            I guess that's all right
            if it's not for too long
        just until I get strong
                just until my bones are
ready again to journey.

You can sleep on my bed. But no squishing me in the night.

        No! Not fair! On mine!

*That's IF you're allowed inside. Uncle Jay can be a
grouch, but Mum is real nice. She's a treasure, you'll
like her. It's just Jay you got to look out for. Just make
sure you stay out from under his feet.*

NEVER KNOWING

PippaPip was right about UncleJay –

                              he *really* doesn't like

                   Dogs.

And I never knew how a Rock thrown

in anger could hurt more than

just your skin.

I run from the Rocks the

                         yelling the pain

but PippaPip and LilaMay don't

run with me.

They stay to swallow his anger whole.

I never knew some wounds

don't heal

by licking.

175

THE WAY OF DOG IS — COMPLICATED

I think I've learned that
even though I'm tangled tight
                    to MyManpup
a heart can be twisted to more than just
one creature.

So how do I follow the River to MyManpup
if MyGirlpups need me to be
here for them
too?

Love Is The
Most Complicated of Beasts.

HAPPINESS IS

When I schnuffle MyGirlpups
coming on the Air
when I sound-snatch the drumming of
their flat-feet running
    I can't help but bark and spin
with all of my
happy.
And we swim and kick the Water
                              splash the Wind and
                chase the Breeze and the whole world
cheers with our joy.
And every day we
scramper and play
together.
So it doesn't matter that UncleJay
hates Dogs
because MyGirlpups are right here
right with me.

ONE DAY I'll GET YOU ...

There are lots of SkyRiverSwimmers in the Water
with their wings flip-flapping

           and beaks yak-quacking
and they tease and taunt with their squawkings.
*Come catch me! Come chase me! You wanna try and
race me? I bet you can't even swim! Ha ha! I bet you
can't even swim!*

I have no choice but to jump on in ...
and it's not really fair

           because I *can* swim –

it's just that I
haven't yet learned
how to fly.

MyGirlpups
laugh every time I try.

A Dog Most Clever

I've thought long and hard
about those SkyRiverSwimmers and
I think they must schnuffle me coming.
Even when I creep-crawl
                  on my belly real low
they still somehow know I am there …
But I've figured out how to
prepare for my ambush for I am A Dog Most Clever.

I've found a great patch
where the SkyRiverSwimmers once hatched out
                      their QuackPups
and it's smudged and sludged full of their tracings.
So I roll.
          And roll.
And I cover my fur with their muckness!
I am a genius! Those SkyRiverSwimmers
won't schnuffle me at all!
They'll think that I'm one of them!

I show MyGirlPups so they know just how
clever I am.
*Look at me! See what I did! Ha ha! Now I'll fool
them! Ha ha!*

179

But MyGirlpups don't clap
                        don't cheer
or pat my back.

Ewww, gross! You stink!

> *Get away! Get back! Pip, make him wash in the river!*

And the SkyRiverSwimmers all quackle with glee.

THE WAY OF DOG — TO LISTEN

At night I creep back
to that house.
UncleJay never finds me
                    never knows I am there
never knows Dogs can grow a
                cold
                    hard   anger.

MyGirlpups never find me
                    never shiver-shake with fear
at me being so near or worry that
I might get hurt.

But somehow Mum spies me.
She wide-eyes me standing guard
with a hard set to my back
to my jaw
            to my thinking and she knows
exactly what it is I am feeling.

She flat-foots silent
                through starlit Grass
and she brings me a plate full of
                                bones.
Good Dog. There you go.
PippaPip was right about Mum.

And she sits in the night
her voice burning bright
whispering all of her fears
inside my *Good Dog* ears because

                              we Dogs
are very good listeners.

We can't stay here much longer. I have to get my girls
away from him. I'd love to take you with us but, you
know, it's so hard to find places to stay and no one
will take us with a dog. You'll be okay, won't you?
You understand, right?

I lay my head in her lap.
I do. There are lots of Uncle Jays in this world. And
it's okay. I've got somewhere I'm supposed to be
anyway.

And I tell her in pictures

                    flitter-flapping through the Air
just where to take HerGirlpups.

I tell her of a place where the Sea meets the Sky
where they can lie in the Sand
where the hot from the Sun will warm them all
through
where they can play in the Waves because now
LilaMay can swim.

And those Waves will pick them up and carry them
and hold them safe
forever and ever and everer.

Hmmmm. Mum sighs and she closes her eyes and she closes
her hand on my paw.
You know, maybe we should go to the beach. I think my girls would like that. What do you reckon?

THE DAY

I spend so many days playing with
MyGirlpups.
Breathing deep
       their whispers
          songs and
        smiles
the warm of their arms
their tossing of Sticks and their cheers when I do
tricks and
their squeals when I lick and lick and lick and lick –
and all the while the cooling of the Breeze and the
dropping of the Leaves
all told me The Day
was getting closer.

So when The Day *does* come

                        The Day They
              Don't Come
I know something must be done
to say goodbye.

Because even though the hard in my gut feels heavier
than a Rock
        a Log
     a Boulder whenever I think of them going –

my tail thumps and spins every time I think
of where it is
they are heading.

NEVER FORGET

My 'Dog' is waiting for me
just where I left it.
Even after all these days
with the maze of Bugs and Beasts crawling

                        trawling across it
the Rain soaking through it –

still it's waiting

                deep deeper deepest
where only the best diggers know
where to find it.

GOODBYE

PippaPip and LilaMay are standing by the car
their faces turned far

                        away from Mum and
the quiet spitting words of Uncle Jay.

I nudge them one by one
their hands clutching my fur
and I tell them **Life is more! Life is more!**

                        and release from my jaw
my 'Dog'.
**So you never forget who I am. So you never forget
who you are. No matter where you are.**

PippaPip scoops the 'Dog' from the ground and
she doesn't make a sound just
wraps herself tight around my neck.
I love you, my boy.

And my heart roars and soars with her
strong and her fierce and with all
of her *Way of Dog* hoping.

      I love you I love you I love you too! cries LilaMay

                              squeezing
and I spin and spin and spin

                     for the journey to begin

with the happy soon to bloom
for MyGirlpups.
LilaMay claps and PippaPip smiles
and then

                        everything
changes.

WOLF FIERCE

We Dogs have good ears for sound-snatching.
But you don't need Dogs' ears to catch the
                                        jeering
                    the yelling
                            the swelling
of UncleJay. His words not quiet
any longer.

And PippaPip and LilaMay start to
                                tremble to
            shake and the breaking of their hearts
turns my mind
black with

                    anger.

Mum is held tight in UncleJay's grip
                his shouts ripping the Air
his bellowing snarls cut like wire.

And my anger GROWWWWWWS
                            bursting and thirsting
                clawing and roaring into a
burning
                    Wolf strong
                            Fierce.

TRUE GROWL

Just one True Growl is all it takes to
shake wide awake
the savage Beasts of my ancestors.
Those Beasts that live inside me still
                just waiting for my will to
bring them back.
To use every bit of fear
                        of anger and despair
to tear apart any question
of my ferocity.
Be strong. Be fierce. Life is more …
And I growl. Long
           deep and
               true
and I leap
        my jaws
           my claws turned to Beast
                  ripping
          gnashing
            slashing with all that
cold anger I've been growing because
                throwing Rocks is one thing
but hurting MyGirlpups and Mum is
quite another.

And UncleJay shrinks to Rabbit before me.

190

I stay and
                make a wall
standing tall
just the way those MammaDogs showed me.

And so.
Mum and PippaPip and LilaMay
they scrabble into that car
and they
                drive

                        away.

My tail thumps *Goodbye. Goodbye. Goodbye.*

ON THE ROAD AGAIN

I only sit for a moment on that road
watching them go
just schnuffling them in for

one last

time.

And I know where I need to be
where I want to be
with all of me racing to get there.
I've just got to keep chasing

keep following that
River to get to the Sea
because you never know what's waiting
on the other side of
morning.

And now MyGirlpups are safe and I am
strong.
My bones are ready.

Too Slow. Again

*Hey! Hi! Hey! Hi! Hey! What are you doing? What's
your name?*

There's a Dog who scrampers flat out towards me
and she's jumping and she's barking
and she's yip-yip-yapping so fast I
can hardly keep up.

*My name's Fuzzy! Fuzzy! Fuzzy! D'you want to
play? D'you want to playplayplay? Come on, come on,
let's play! Hey?Hey?Hey?*

She's just a little pup and her whirling tail
twirls circles in the Air
and she's slapping her paws on the ground so
I can't help but scramper around and around
and I slap my paws on her chest and for a moment
we are lost in
     a blur of fur
of wrestles and rumbles of
Pure Dog Delight.

**Thanks, Fuzzy, but I've got to go. I'm following the
River to the Sea where maybe MyManpup will be.
Maybe.**

The River? The Sea? That sounds fun! Will you take
me? Please please please? Pleasepleaseplease?

But then –
a loop of sharp wire is thrown around my neck
and the fighting from my paws
                              the snapping of my jaws
just pulls that wire tighter
around my throat.

   Gotcha! This the one you called us about, mister?

Fuzzy wide-eyes me
her body scrunched low and her
whimpers and whines set her trembling.
Not the Ranger! Not the Ranger! That's Danger
Danger Danger!

This is The Ranger? *This* is The Van?
The Van you never come back from?
Run, Fuzzy! Run! The Way of Dog is to Run!

She looks at me with

     eyes so big so

        wide so

    sad they are
    drowning.

Then she's gone.

And there's a schnuffle in the Air
of shoe-leg anger and of hate
and the sour

　　　　　　sticky sweat of UncleJay.

*Yeah, that's the one. He's real vicious. Look – this is
where he bit me. He would have attacked the kids too
if I hadn't stopped him. He needs to be destroyed.*

　　　　　*Well, thanks for calling it in. Strays like
　　　　　this are too dangerous to be roaming about.
　　　　　We'll deal with him.*

And UncleJay snarls
and he runs a thick finger across his thick neck
　　　　　crrrrrrkkkkkk
while that Ranger prods and pokes and
that wire keeps on choking

　　　　　　and she shoves me
　　　　　roughs me tumbles me into
The Van.

STONE CAGES

REDRIPWRAP

They cut my RedRipWrap
from around my neck

                           and now I can't schnuffle

MyManpup
here with me
at all.

Now MyManpup isn't
here with me
at all.

And I am nowhere
at all
without MyManpup.

CAGE AGAIN

It seems to me that maybe my life is
meant to be lived
in a cage.
Maybe life isn't really much
more than a concrete floor
after all.

I don't try
the food they slide my way
or play with the balls that they give me.

I don't try
to catch the eye
of anyone.

I wish they would leave me alone.

Sometimes

Sometimes
when the Sun in my eyes
deafens the cries of other Dogs
in their cages
my mind flies me back.
Back to under the Trees with MyManpup
who talks as we walk
                        with love a fierce ache
that never can break or
be taken.

Sometimes
when I schnuffle the night
and the Wind wraps me tight
if the Breeze is just right
my mind flies me back.
Back to a street with a Fox who makes me
his friend and defends me
                        from those whose hoping
                                whose caring
was lost long ago.

Sometimes
when the Skies burst wide open with Rain
and the sound-snatch of Water
rushes the drain

my mind flies me back.
Back to a River with small arms around my neck
so true and so tight and the swirls
            of MyGirlpup's legs against mine
sends tingles of happy
all through my spine.

And my mind flies me back to soft hands in the cold
to strange shoe-legs that throw all that silver and gold
            into a cap when I dance for OldOne.
Those hands playing that StringThing
those songs that could sing me a
whole new world full of dreaming.

And my mind flies me back to long chats
with a greedy FatRat
            the close of ScratchCat
and the whispers of all
the MammaDogs.
And the whisper of
my mamma.

Sometimes
my mind flies me back and
the ache in my heart in
                    my bones in
my blood
is just

           a little less
just
for a moment.

But it isn't enough to lift my head
to lift my eyes to the Skies or
hope that maybe things will work out
Someday.

Because I think I will break
if my heart starts to ache any

harder.

Done

So when a woman who carries the warm of the
Sun in her voice
who schnuffles of Flowers
                    of Mud and of Rain
comes and tries to calm my pain
            I turn away to say
Leave me be.

But she whispers how she works here
in this Lost and Found Pound
            how they know I'm no danger
                        how that Ranger was wrong
            to even think so.

*I saw you on the news. That was you, wasn't it? You
knew that old woman was sick. You fetched the doctors.
You wouldn't hurt a flea, would you, boy?*

And she promises to find me a home
so I don't roam the streets any longer.

But I don't want
anything
            anymore.

                                    I'm done.

THE WAY OF DOG IS NO MORE

It's been a long time
on this concrete floor. Each Moon that
rises each Sun that soars
doesn't bring me any more
hoping.

And the shoe-legs are saying I can't be staying
for much longer.
I've seen other Dogs
taken away when there's nowhere else
for them to stay and I know
what this means.
They must have a great big DeadDogBin
somewhere.
But I feel no sadness
                              no fear.
I am almost
not really
here
anymore

              anyway.

STiRRiNGS

That SunWoman keeps coming back.
Again and again and again.

*I won't let you give up, you know. The vet reckons
you're probably only two, maybe three. You've got your
whole doggy life ahead of you. Anyway, I've sorted the
perfect thing for you.*

She scruffles my fur and
                 nuzzles my head
and I'm trying so hard
not to listen.

*So, there's this program, called Pets in Prisons. And the
way it works is that you go live with one of the men
in the prison, and that man trains you up to be an
Assistance Dog, and when you can do everything right,
you graduate and go help someone who really needs a
dog just like you in their life.*

She pats my head and plays with my fur
and I push away the stirring deep inside.

*You're a pretty special dog, you know. And I think in
this life there is more than just one person who needs
you to be there for them. And anyway …*

she smiles and kisses my paw
... there is more to life than this old concrete floor.
You'll see.

CRATE

There are nine of us Dogs
brought into The Prison
                    in cages the shoe-legs call
crates.
Like a crate is somehow greater than a cage.
But even though the name is not the same
                                                    the size is
                                    not
much different.

They tell us not to fear
            that we're all safe here but
we all know how this story goes.
We will not be fooled by life again.

Go Away

There are nine men waiting for us nine
Dogs crating
but there's only one man who
                        wide-eyes right at me
right across the sea of Dogs and of
faces.
He's holding a bowl and a bag full of treats
and he flat-feet shuffles my way. I turn my head to say
Go away
and he turns his head away too.
I don't think this man knows what to do
either.

Everyone find the dog assigned to you and introduce
yourselves. Hurry up! This shouldn't take all day.
The shouty shoe-leg woman's voice is
hard and is sharp and
I wide-eye the man shy at her words.

All around other men are
                        opening crates but still
this man

                                                waits.

Good. I don't want anything to
do with him

with this place.
And he doesn't want anything to
do with me either.
I can schnuffle it all over his skin.

All around other Dogs are schnuffling their men
are nuzzling and snuffling and scruffling their men.
I turn in my crate so all I wide-eye
is the wall.

*Charlie! Are you part of this program or not? If you
don't want to be here there's a long list of men waiting
to take your place. Get over to that dog and get it out of
that crate! Now!*

I sound-snatch the shuffle of his feet
and schnuffle his scared and unknowing.

I don't know if the dog wants to come out …
and his voice is gruff and is
trembling.

*Were you even paying attention in class? Offer the dog
your hand. Talk to him. Get him out of that crate. If
you're not going to put in the effort, you can go back to
your cell.*

No, wait – I am. I'll … try.

The whole room quiets
                    every man
            every Dog
their eyes all stuck on my crate.
I turn around and wait to see what happens.

CHARLIEMAN

Hey. So, uh. What do they call you then?
His eyes are darting and he
chews on his lip
            and he holds his hand up to my snout.
It doesn't schnuffle of anything
special.

I'm Charlie. Do you, um, want to come out of that
cage? I know it's noisy out here, but. Anyway.

CharlieMan is crouched down
            creased up and
crumpled his
head scooping low

folding small even though he's really
quite
        tall.
And he opens my door and my
paw finds his hand
                but I never
planned on doing that.
I pull it back so there is no
question
of my intention.

He wide-eyes me
and
there's something
in the way he
sighs that
tugs.
But I don't care.
I don't. I don't
care at all. I show with my tail all rigid
my body turned hard and my head turned away that
I am not interested in staying.
That I am not interested
in him
not even a bit.

I only come out of my crate
for the treat.

Nights in Prison

I'm dreaming of MyManpup
of his screaming and his cries
of the schnuffle of his skin of
his scared

        his surprise

           of the ache in my legs when I am too

    slow

        too far
too hopeless to help him.

And I wake in my crate to
the shaking of the bed

          next to mine
to the CharlieMan dreaming and screaming

             in fright at the sights

        crept into his *own* head.
And waves of scared schnuffle off him.

I wonder what it is he is dreaming.
I wonder what fears have grown in his bones.
I wonder if he has lost a manpup
of his own.

UNDERSTANDINGS

I guess it's not so bad in here.
It's just another place to be.
I suppose.
And that CharlieMan seems to know

                                     a little

about Dogs after all.
He knows exactly where to scratch to get at
that itch that niggles and scriggles my skin
                  and he scritches me under my chin.

And I don't know how he does it
but when he throws the ball
he makes it roll just
                perfect.

And the way he strokes my fur
                      rubs my belly
                pats my head
makes a quivering sort of warm spread right
through me.

He's nice, this CharlieMan.
And he's kind of quiet and kind of

                                 sad

but I guess
I am A Dog Who Gets It.

And I think
                    somehow
he is a man who kind of
gets Dogs too.

Sweet Dreams

We both wake in the night

                                again
from our own dreaming frights

                                again
and CharlieMan reaches his hand
through my crate to calm me.

You're meant to stay in that cage at night. It's part of
your training. But I guess it won't hurt to let you out.
I don't like being locked up either. I hope I'm making
the right decision. I'm not altogether so good at making
the right decisions. But here …

                                and he opens up my crate
… if you want to come out and, I don't know, snuggle
up for a bit, you can.

Doesn't he know? It is *always* the right decision
to snuggle a Dog tight

                especially at night
for A Snuggle with a Dog Will Always Bring
Sweet Dreams and Great Happiness. That is
The Way of Dog.

And his chest
is the best pillow I've
ever slept on.

WORKING? WHAT'S WORKING?

Who knew that CharlieMan could be so much fun
when he's not going on about
work to be done
but doesn't he know that work should never
                    take over from play?
I think I'd forgotten the wonderous way
play tingles my skin and makes the whole day
so much brighter.
I wonder if CharlieMan has forgotten that too.

Dog. Are you listening?

**Sure am, CharlieMan. Hey, would you look at that!
A fly! And it's buzzing around my eye and just give
me a second so I can snap it … Wait – there it goes!
Wait – there it goes! Wait – aww. I missed it.**

Come here, Dog! Are you paying attention?

**Hey, let's go down to the grass where the other Dogs
go and I'll show them everything I've taught you.
I don't think any of their shoe-legs can roll a ball the
way you do. How do you get it to spin like that so it
always changes direction? It's very clever, you know.**

No. Put down the leash. We're here to work. If I can't teach you what's in this folder, then we're both up the creek without a paddle. We're already behind. Come on. I know you're smart. You just got to listen.

I'm all ears, CharlieMan.

Look – there's a light switch on the wall. All you got to do is jump up and press it. Okay? Follow the treat. Here. Come on. Up here! Up!

But you don't need a light in the day, CharlieMan! Come on, let's go play! Here's my leash! Here's my ball! Can't you sound-snatch me at all? You need to move away from the wall so we can play! Are you sound-snatching anything I say?

No! Not up on me! Up on the wall! The wall! It's like you're not listening at all.

SHOE-LEG BRAINS

There's something making CharlieMan sad.
I don't know why he's worried and so
hurried and so stressed
but he throws down his folder and
crumples on the floor and starts to
whimper.
I'm hopeless. I'm sorry, Dog. I don't know what I'm
doing wrong. I can never do anything right.

And now he is sighing
                   whisper wailing
            creaky crying and
CharlieMan? CharlieMan?
he holds tight to my fur and he

                              shudders.

It's okay. It's okay, CharlieMan.

Some shoe-legs say that
way way way back in the day
they were the ones to tame us Dogs. But
we know it was us Dogs that tamed those shoe-legs.
We know how shoe-leg brains can
get a little messed
a little stressed a little cluttered with
                   mutters that don't matter

but all that natter in their minds just
clatters up their thinking

                                    and twists and turns
                        and
tumbles so their thoughts all spill and rumble

but we Dogs know how to still
a brain to
quiet.

We Dogs know
how to calm

            how a wet black
            snout in the palm
            of a hand
        a head in a lap
a paw on a knee
can be all the difference
                in the world.
It's one of *The Ways of Dog.*
It's okay, MyCharlieMan.
I'm here. I understand.

Counting Backwards. Again

There were nine Dogs here to begin with.
And then there were eight because they said
Sputnik was
so great that she was ready to be given a
new Family.
They gave her a big party
and a new squeaky toy and a fancy new bed

and
everything.

My toy doesn't even squeak
anymore. Not after I so
expertly killed it.

And then there were six because Chase and Missy
were both chosen for their skills
and their shoe-legs were so thrilled
that the happy schnuffled off them in
waves.
I wish I could make MyCharlieMan happy like that.

It's not so much fun playing on the Grass when
our numbers keep dwindling.
And now there are four, no, three
and I'm beginning to see a pattern.

Charlie! Have you taught that dog anything yet?

ShoutyShoe-LegWoman always makes me shiver
                  makes MyCharlieMan quiver and
drop his eyes.
*You've got one more week. If there is no improvement,
you are OUT of the program!*

        We're trying—

*And that dog goes back to the pound! Does he even
know how to carry yet? Show me.*
And she throws her hat at MyCharlieMan.

        Well, we've been working on …

Carry? Did she say *carry*?
**Leave it to me, MyCharlieMan. That's easy.
MyManpup taught me the hat trick when I was a
pup. See? Why didn't you ask me this earlier?**

*Hmm. It's a start. But why is that dog walking on his
hind legs like a fool? You're not training a circus dog. If
I were you, Charlie, I'd start taking this seriously. That
dog is useless if he can't graduate the program.*

MyCharlieMan shrinks down small.
        Don't listen, he whispers, *you're not useless.*
I do not like ShoutyShoe-LegWoman
                                    at all.

GETTING SERIOUS

MyCharlieMan and me are
getting serious.

*We'll show her how clever you are. I won't let her send
you back to the pound. I won't! She can't! She—*

But he's flittery and fluttery
              his mind all clattery cluttery
and I need to show him how
to slow

                         how to settle
         how to calm his shoe-leg brain
so I can explain what he needs to do
    to make him feel good.

**Play will help you feel better, MyCharlieMan. Let's
go outside. You can throw the ball – that always makes
you smile.**

*Come on, Dog. Show me you can do it and then we can
play. And what is it with all that spinning? You need
to learn to slow, to settle, to calm your body. This work
will make you feel good, Dog. It's play for your brain.
Do you get it?*

Huh. Okay. **Whatever you say, MyCharlieMan.**

I put my paw on his hand so he knows

                             I understand and we

      slow.

And we

      settle.

And we

      calm.

But his eyes are still too big and too wild
and I wonder …
*Is it too dark in here for you, MyCharlieMan? Even
though it's day? Wait. Let me turn the light on, okay?*

You did it! Clever Dog! You turned on the light!

*Of course! Why didn't you say that's what you needed
before?*

EVERY TIME

I get what MyCharlieMan wanted to say
when he said there was work to be done –
helping and working *is* fun
                          it is just learning tricks
            just another way to play
another way for that
happy to tingle my skin and to
make the whole day so much brighter.
MyCharlieMan sure is clever.

Now when MyCharlieMan points to the wall
I know to stand tall
            and flip the switch with my snout
to help MyCharlieMan out.
And he smiles with a brightness deep inside him.
Every time.

And when he points with his finger
at a closed cupboard door
I know for sure that he wants me to open it.
Because that's where he hides all my treats.
And he gives me one. Every time.

And when in the day
he pretends that he's sleeping

                          although I can

                              schnuffle he's not
when he starts screaming and
pretending he's dreaming
I pull at the covers and nudge him
to wake.
Wakey, wakey! It's time for a cuddle!
And we do. Every time.

And when he falls on the ground
I sound the alarm with my paw
and shoe-legs come running
all tummy rubbing
and tell me
how clever I am.
And MyCharlieMan stands.
Yes, Dog. Yes!
***Let's go to the Grass now so I can tell whoever is left
how good you did.***
And we do. Every time.

And he sits in a chair that rolls on big wheels
and he feels me walking beside him
                              slow and settled and calm
and I open the doors
and I carry his bag
and pick up his keys when he drops them.
And he holds me. And he whispers
Goooood Dog! You are amazing!

Every time.

And when he says *Steady*, I turn hard and
get ready so he can push himself up on my back.
And I help him to walk nice and
s   l   o   w
and I show him where to go
so his flat-feet don't stumble where the floor has all
crumbled and cracked.
Yes! Good guiding! That's my Dog.
It's like our minds are
one.

And I think that MyCharlieMan gets
what I wanted to say
when I said he should remember the wonderous way
that play makes the whole day much brighter –
because we play now
                    every day now
and he rolls that ball in the way
no one else ever can.
Yes! Good rolling! That's MyCharlieMan.
Every time.

A Dog with a Job to Do

MyCharlieMan says there's just one thing left
before I am ready to graduate.
We've been going on excursions
so they know that no diversion will ever
distract me.
Because MyCharlieMan says that
I am A Dog with a Job to Do.

No shoe-legs whizzing by
on two spinning wheels that feel
                    so good in my teeth
can fill me with that desperate need to
               match their speed to
chase them down
          race them down
                  hold them down
anymore.
For I am A Dog with a Job to Do.

No traces left on posts
no Dogs wanting to play
no SkyRiverSwimmers can ever
tempt me away because
I am A Dog with a Job to Do.

And all the shoe-legs tap tap tapping
don't bother me at all

                all their
          squishing and
                their squashing
             their pushing and their mushing
and their stepping on my paws
won't even ache my jaws into
whining
          because
I am A Dog with a Job to Do.

And MyCharlieMan pats me
          and scratches my belly
and everything is just
perfect.

Okay! Here we go, Dog. This is it. Good heeling. Good
steadying. Good carrying. Now—
Whoa. Where are we going? Wait. I know that
schnuffle on the Air. Wait, you aren't wanting to
go THERE, are you, MyCharlieMan? No no no!
No no no! Do you want to get SMUNCHED?
NONONONONO!
It's okay, Dog. It's just a train. Don't worry about it.
Don't worry about it? Don't worry? DON'T
WORRY?!

And there is that rumbling

        that tumbling

               and it's growing and

            growing and

              GRO**WING**

***AND THE SNAKINGMETALMUNCHER IS
HERE TO
EAT US AND CRUNCH US AND TAKE US IN
ITS JAWS AND SMUNCH—***

Dog. Listen to me. Slow. Settle. Calm.

And I do.

You trust me, don't you?

And I do.

*I won't ever put you in danger. I need you to do this for
me. Your person will need you to do this for them too.
Will you do this for me? Can you?*

MyManpup wanted me to do

              this for him too. And I couldn't.

And I didn't. And

         and

             and

and MyCharlieMan's hand on my back on
                    my head on
            my fur
makes me sure that

                                        maybe
                just maybe
I can swallow
        my scared.
Because MyCharlieMan needs me to.

Now remember. You've got a job to do. Dog, get me on
that train.

And I do.

GRADUATING

ShoutyShoe-LegWoman cheers and she claps
and she pats me on my back
and she squeezes MyCharlieMan's shoulder.
I knew you could do it. You just had to believe in
yourself as much as you believed in that dog.

And MyCharlieMan smiles and he
whoops and he
                    scoops me up in his arms.

Dog! You did it! You did it!

How about that? The slowest dog ever to graduate.
Charlie, you'd better get that dog all washed and ready
to go. His person has been waiting a long time.

Already? Oh. Okay. When's he go?

First thing tomorrow.

ACHING

How can I bear to go out there again
                              to a life
without MyCharlieMan?

How can these shoe-legs keep growing
                              their roots deep inside my
                heart
        only to leave me
when I love them
                when I need them so much?
Don't they know?
I don't want them
                        to

                        go.

We lay down our heads in MyCharlieMan's bed
together for one
last
                night.
And MyCharlieMan tells of the life I'll be living of
                helping a kid
whose thoughts cannot settle
                who finds it hard to talk

who finds it hard to walk
and who thinks and feels and hopes
a world of wonders.

*And the kid uses one of those chairs with wheels, just like
the ones we practised with. I bet they'll be better than me
in it. They probably won't even run over your paws. And
this kid was a victim of crime, so it's kind of nice, isn't it,
that me in prison can help make things kind of right.*

MyCharlieMan buries his head in my fur
and he holds me.

*I didn't think I could do it, you know. I didn't think I
could really do anything much anymore. But I always
knew you could do it. You just needed a little time was
all. I guess sometimes we all just need a little time, hey,
Dog?*

And I lick and lick and lick until he
smiles.

*You know, I was thinking, when I get out of here, I'd
like to work in the program on the outside too. Help
other dogs, other people. What do you think?*

I hope he can see what I'm trying to say in that
way we Dogs do with our eyes

because sometimes it's too hard to show
to let them know
just how much
    we understand.
You are MyMan, MyCharlieMan.
You are forever MyMan.

Goodbye

And so it ends.
And so my heart bends and twists and turns and I
yearn for just a little longer.
But I know I must be stronger
for MyCharlieMan.

There is so much world out there, Dog. Just waiting for
us. I think I'd forgotten how beautiful the world can be.

His tears fall warm
and my head rests on his chest
but I feel my heart breaking
into splinters too small to
ever fix.

Come now, my beautiful Dog. Don't you know?
I do. I know. I've heard.

And inside my blood churns at his words.

Life is more than this old concrete floor.

And he kisses my head.
Be strong, Dog.

And they take me

away
from MyCharlieMan.

COMING
HOME

LONG DRIVE

It's a long drive in that crate
                              in that van
taking me from MyCharlieMan
who loved me and taught me and showed me
himself.
Myself.
Ourselves entwined.

It's a long drive in that crate
                              in that van
where all I can think of
is how I can't stand to keep loving
keep

                                        breaking

so many many many
times.

And when we stop I wonder
how much of me
is left for a kid
whose thoughts cannot settle who
needs me. So they reckon.

It's a long drive.
And then
              it is over.

THE ARRIVAL

The van door opens and the Wind from outside
carries a schnuffle
        that shimmers in my snout
that shouts of deep futures and of
even deeper
                rememberings.

Traces that dip
        that flow and that whirl
that twirl through the Air
and for a moment I'm scared that I'm
                   mistaken.

Because it can't be.

There's no way it can be—

IS THAT YOU?

Scruff.
Scruff
  ity?

MyManpup?

Scruffity?

MyManpup? MyManpup?
      Scruffity! Is
    it
  you?

**MyManpup! It's me! I'm your Dog! I'm your Dog!
It's me! I'm Scruffity! I'm your Dog!!!**

WHEN ONLY A SPIN WILL DO

There is no way to explain the twirling whirling
explosion in your heart your

                              brain your

                 bones your

                                     blood your

skin your

            fur

            when you see again

                      your manpup

who you thought was gone forever.

                  There's only one thing to do.

                      And who knew that a chair

                      on wheels

                            could spin in utter

                            happiness too?

                        MyManpup

                          he spins Proper Dog.

The Way of Dog – Family

MyManpup schnuffles of a million happy *Nows*
and a thousand and one
Soon Will Be dreams
and he wraps me in his arms and he
yowls. A sobbing kind of howl for everything
that's been for all the feelings that he has
been holding. And I
fold myself over his body.
It's okay. I'm here. I get it.

His body it schnuffles of hurt and of pain and
                                                            of broken

but I am not
just a pup now
            and this is a hurt that I know now
how to help.

And we tip our heads to the Sky
and we howl of our *Now* and our *Always* together.
And we howl as our hearts and our souls carry

                                                            high

and we watch our song fly us
                        wherever
                we want to be.

For that
is the brilliance of a howl
of a Manpup and his Dog.
Together again.

HOME

MyManpup and AuntyChris and me
live all together in our home by the Sea
and we watch the River flow
by our window.

And I help MyManpup do
                         anything he needs to do
                                anything he wants to
                do
just like MyCharlieMan taught me to
because
I am A Dog with a Job to Do
                    and because
I am MyManpup's Scruffity.

Forever

Every day MyManpup and me
we go to the Beach
where the Sea meets the Sky
and we lie in the Sand and the
hot from the Sun warms us through.
And we swim in those Waves and they
pick us up and hold us safe.
Together.

And the Trees stretch
    and the Clouds loop and
SkySingers flip-flap-flip-flap-swoop
    and the Wind whishing by in the big open Sky
carries our dreams so high in her wings
    and each moment sings only of happy.

For this is *The Way of Dog*.
Me and MyManpup.
Together. Forever. Foreverer.

Acknowledgements

Scruffity first wandered up to me a few years ago, when I was deep in the middle of writing another book. He rested his head on my lap, gave me a lick, and offered to take me for a much-needed walk. How could I possibly resist? From that moment forward, his presence, and the journey he has taken me on, has led me to experience the world in wonderfully new and enchanting ways. He taught me to see the world from a 'Dog's point of snout'. To look more closely at the world around me, to pay attention to *all* my senses and, most importantly, to slow down and enjoy the small moments of happiness.

Scruffity did have help, though. My two dogs, Moomin and Tishkin, were not only my constant writing companions, keeping my feet warm and nudging my arm away from the computer when I had been sitting too long – but they also became my guides into the worlds and ways of dogs. They showed me just which trees were important, which fences to avoid, how to sniff the messages on the wind and to listen to the language of the birds, and why one should always roll in the grass after the rain. To Moomin and Tishkin, and to all the brilliant dogs that have journeyed with me so far – Trapper, Scout, Harry and Willy – thank you for your unconditional love, for always listening, for always being there, for showing me The Way, and for making me just a little bit more dog.

And to all the shoe-legs who have made this book possible – thank you! To the brilliant people at UQP who saw in Scruffity the same thing I did, thank you for inviting us so warmly into your pack. Huge thanks especially to Clair Hume and Cathy Vallance – every moment of this adventure has been an absolute joy and delight. With your expert guidance, this book has become so much more than I ever thought possible. Thank you for all the questions, conversations, suggestions and experimentations, and for believing utterly in the voice of a dog. And an extra big thank you to the amazing Sean Buckingham, for bringing Scruffity to life so vividly and truly. From your very first sketch, I knew that no one else would be able to capture the Scruffitiness of this book the way you could. Here is hoping for the opportunity to create many more books with you. Thanks also to Hannah Janzen for the brilliant cover design, to Jean Smith and Sally Wilson, and to all the other hands and minds at UQP that have brought this book into being.

Thanks to my wonderful agent Claire Wilson, for loving Scruffity from the get-go, and for never giving up on finding him the perfect home. And to my writing community who have kept me going, kept me believing, kept me inspired and excited and who continuously show me new ways to hone my craft. As always, many thanks go to the countless librarians and booksellers who have, time after time, managed to find just the books I need at just the right time. The world would surely end without you wonderful people. And a special thanks to my Coven – Penny Harrison, Kate Mildenhall and Penni Russon, thank you for the magic.

Thank you also to the traditional custodians of the lands that nurtured this book into being. The lands on which it was conceived, written, lived and walked, the unceded, ancestral lands of the Wurundjeri and Turrbal peoples. Always was, always will be.

And finally, to my family who make it all possible. Luca, Mischa, Mina and Jugs. You are my world. Forever. Forerever.

 Zana Fraillon is an internationally acclaimed, multi-award-winning author of books for children and young adults. Her work has been published in over 15 countries and is in development for both stage and screen. She has degrees in history and teaching and is currently undertaking a PhD in Creative Writing at LaTrobe University. Zana's passion for empowering young people to find their voice is a feature of both her books and her work with writers of all ages.

WILDOAK by C. C. HARRINGTON

Maggie's stutter makes going to school hard. She will do almost anything to avoid speaking in class – even if that leads to trouble.

Sent to stay in the depths of Cornwall with a grandfather she barely knows, Maggie discovers an abandoned snow leopard hiding in nearby Wildoak Forest. Sheltered by the ancient trees, the two of them build an understanding in secret. But when the cub is spotted by local villagers, danger follows – threatening everything she has come to believe in.

Can Maggie find an answer before time runs out – not just for the cub, but for herself and the forest as well?

Enchanting and thrilling . . .
PIERS TORDAY

Paperback, ISBN 978-1-915026-14-9, £7.99 • ebook, ISBN 978-1-915026-19-4, £7.99

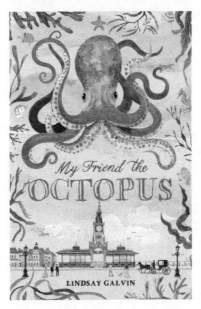

MY FRIEND THE OCTOPUS by LINDSAY GALVIN

ENGLAND, 1893

Twelve-year-old Vinnie Fyfe loves to draw the fancy hats created by her mother, a high-society milliner. However, her life changes abruptly when she's sent away to her aunt's in Brighton, where she takes comfort from sketching the sea creatures at the local aquarium.

Here, Vinnie forms a special bond with a recently acquired giant octopus, which leads her in turn to new friends: Charlie, an aspiring reporter, and Temitayo, the ward of an English gentleman keen to carve her own path.

But the strength of their friendship is put to the test with the arrival of a sinister visitor, who entangles them all in a most dangerous mystery . .

Galvin is a thrilling storyteller . . .
THE TELEGRAPH

Paperback, ISBN 978-1-913696-40-5, £7.99 • ebook, ISBN 978-1-913696-73-3, £7.99

BY ASH, OAK AND THORN by MELISSA HARRISON

Three little people wake from their winter sleep in an old ash tree. Moss, Burnet and Cumulus usually love spring, but their joy turns to worry when they discover that Cumulus is starting to fade away.

The trio set off in search of answers, only to discover that they must travel far beyond the countryside to a loud, busy and danger-filled place called The Hive . . .

Timely and magical . . .
NATASHA FARRANT

Paperback, ISBN 978-1-913322-12-0, £7.99 • ebook, ISBN 978-1-913322-94-6, £7.99